The Joy of
CHRISTMAS

The Joy of
Christmas

Edited by

Llewellyn Miller

THE **BOBBS-MERRILL** COMPANY, INC.
A SUBSIDIARY OF HOWARD W. SAMS & CO., INC.
Publishers · INDIANAPOLIS · NEW YORK

COPYRIGHT © 1960 BY THE BOBBS-MERRILL COMPANY, INC.

PRINTED IN THE UNITED STATES OF AMERICA

FIRST EDITION

LIBRARY OF CONGRESS CATALOG CARD NUMBER: 60-12630

CONTENTS

INTRODUCTION

CHRISTMAS is so many moods and memories . . .
Christmas is the glitter of trees hung with shining ornaments.
Christmas is the perfume of pine, roasting turkey and flaming
pudding. Christmas is the festive color of poinsettias, holly
berries and candy canes.

Christmas is the sound of carols, hymns and the busy cling of
Salvation Army Santa Claus bells mingling with the teeth-grit-
ting of harassed clerks, belated shoppers and weary postmen.

Christmas is a chore, a festivity, a feast, a month-long mad-
ness and the best day of the year.

Christmas is the glow in the eyes of a believing child.

Christmas is a birthday.

All of these aspects of Christmas are dealt with in this collection. Most of the stories are light-hearted. Some are tender and
touching as well as funny. One is a mystery. One is a staggering
recipe that is both conversation piece and gourmet's delight.
One is a thought-provoking fable. But all have a common
appeal. All are good for reading out loud.

The backlog of writings about Christmas is enormous. At first
thought the compiling of an anthology of stories of appeal to
both young and old seems the easiest of tasks. It soon becomes
clear that not too many Christmas tales written in the past have
much meaning for readers of today except as commentary on
social changes. The impact of the sorrows of little match girls
homeless on Christmas Eve, of widowed seamstresses too poor
to buy porridge let alone presents, and of old people on the
way to the poor-house has disappeared with the forgotten man.
In their day such stories served well to remind the reader that

Christmas is a time for sharing with others. Times change, but the spirit of Christmas does not. The best stories of today carry the same warming message with a different cast of characters.

One of the things that impresses the researcher in this field is the high percentage of stories emphasizing the dire fates that befall those who ignore the true meaning of Christmas, trifle with its traditions or take any punitive action against Santa Claus.

This is true of most of the memorable stories—old and new, humorous or sober—from the most beloved of all, Dickens' *A Christmas Carol*, written over a hundred years ago, to Bob Considine's recent "Well, A Little More Time . . . ," Ogden Nash's merry rhyme about the horrible end of "The Boy Who Laughed at Santa Claus" and John D. MacDonald's "Open Before Christmas."

Many of the stories selected for this book appeared in magazines and after a month disappeared with the brittle tree and the dusty tinsel. Others first appeared in books now out of print. But all have special meaning for the reader of today, so it is a double pleasure to give them the more permanent place they deserve within the covers of this book.

LLEWELLYN MILLER

The Joy of
CHRISTMAS

Mr. West was no Scrooge. He did not say "Bah! Humbug!" to everything about Christmas.

But he did think the celebration was getting a little out of hand.

So the family voted to skip the huge tree, the lavish decorations, the expensive ribbons and wrappings, the traditional turkey—and have a sensible Christmas.

By *John D. MacDonald*

OPEN BEFORE CHRISTMAS

THREE weeks before Christmas Benjamin West made a policy decision, not without argument from the other Wests. He was wearing his favorite and disreputable Sunday afternoon costume of baggy gray slacks and the wool shirt with the big green and black checks. He sat in the living-room chair, looking as if he had been dropped there casually from some great height. Helen, his pretty and durable and intuitive wife, had been aware of the intensity of his long silence and it had made her uneasy. She had looked where he was looking—out the picture window at a soggy, gray snowfall, at the other trim homes in the Riverbanks section—and found no clue.

George was following his twelve-year-old Sunday routine, cutting, fitting and shaping balsa on the worktable in his bedroom, emerging astench with airplane glue to catch an occasional television program.

Kathy was down the street doing fifteen-year-old homework with a girl friend with, no doubt, the usual full quota of telephone interruptions.

When Kathy came home, snow melting on her dark hair, Ben demanded a gathering of the clan in the living room without television. Helen, Kathy and George were understandably a

11

bit nervously alert. There had been other policy meetings.

"Understand me now," Ben said rather sententiously. "I am not saying Bah, nor am I saying Humbug."

"What is a humbug anyway, Dad?" George asked.

"Later, boy. I don't want my own family to think that I am deficient in Christmas spirit. I still have it, but it's a fight. I mean that down at the shop we have to dream up campaigns and copy to make people buy more, spend more at Christmas time. All the ceremony and everything was just fine when you kids were little, but if we all think it over calmly and carefully, I think you will see that I am right when I say it is time for us to get off the old-fashioned type Christmas kick."

"Just what do you mean, dear?" Helen asked.

He made an inclusive gesture. "You know. A big monster of a tree. Tree trimming. Wrapping everything. Turkey dinner. The old Lionel Barrymore records."

"What do we cut down to?"

"I don't see why we can't have a nice little table tree. Maybe a steak dinner. And why wrap all the stuff we buy each other? Two sheets of fancy paper for two bits and a lot of work and then—*whooom*. Take George. He can get through the ribbons and down to the meat in three milliseconds. And no red bow on Twombley. It makes that cat act degraded and humiliated. I expect him to break out into a nervous giggle."

Kathy spoke languidly. "But would this be fair actually to George? After all."

"Oh, blop!" said George.

"We are," Kathy said to George, "of different generations, in a manner of speaking."

"You're running those generations through here pretty fast, dear," Helen said. She turned toward her son. "Does she have a point? Would you feel wrong about Christmas if this one were—different?"

"Not so long as I get the bike."

"And that," his father said, "is a practical attitude, but eminently selfish, George boy. But it puts your vote on my side. Up to this point we need one more for a majority."

"He should still have only a half vote," Kathy said.

"You got your full vote at twelve," Helen reminded her.

"I believe I was considerably older at that age. Might I ask, Dad, is this an attempt to—reduce expenses?"

"Your father," Ben said, "is making out just fine. Not stupendous, but adequate. This isn't to save money. It's to—look at the whole thing objectively and knock off the pointless parts of the routine. We'll have plenty of Christmas spirit. We'll be surrounded by it. We shouldn't ever as a family let ourselves get trapped into—too much tradition." He turned to Helen. "How is your vote?" he asked.

"Abstaining," Helen said.

"No opinion at all?" Ben asked.

"I don't believe I care to state it."

He looked at her a bit dubiously and then said, "Okay. Of the voting members George and I form a two-thirds majority. Care to state an opinion, Kath?"

"Many aspects of our Christmas routine are corny, Dad. I vote with you."

"Settled," he said. George scuttled back to his glue. Ben picked up a magazine. Helen picked up her mending. Kathy drifted to the telephone, where three minutes later she was chortling at the normal inanities.

When Helen looked up, Ben was again staring out the window.

"More policies?" she asked.

"Huh? No. What in the world *is* a humbug?"

"Ben, are you sure of—all this?"

"Yes, dear. I'm positive. We'll have a fine Christmas."

Ben brought the tree home on Friday, the twenty-first, when he came home from work. It looked rather like a small folding umbrella.

"Here's the tree, honey," he said.

"Oh, I didn't see it at first."

He stood it on the kitchen table, holding it by the middle.

"Do you think those little branches will come down?"

"Sure. Look when I hold them down. It has a nice shape, hasn't it?"

"Very charming. Will we put lights on it?"

"One of the little strings. It'll go on the table by the living-room door. On one end. And then we can pile the presents on the other end. Tell the kids they can decorate it any time."

"It shouldn't take long," Helen said. "Oh, the box from Mother came today."

"That's another thing. This do-not-open-until routine. I see no reason why we can't split the loot tonight, do you?"

"I guess that would be in keeping with the new order."

Ben looked at her suspiciously but Helen maintained a bland expression. That evening after dinner George got the box of Christmas decorations out of the storage room behind the garage. As he carried it in, his legs showed under it, the bristled crest of his butch cut over the top of it. He set it down with the exaggerated sigh that terminated all manual effort. Helen had erected the tree on the table. It looked slightly apologetic. George and Kathy delved into the box.

"How about these?" Kathy asked. She held up the window wreaths.

"Ask your father," Helen said.

Ben frowned at the wreaths. "Better hang them, baby. Our new policy is our own business but we don't want all of Riverbanks saying we've goofed off on the neighborhood decorations."

So the wreaths went on the door and in the front windows.

Later Ben became aware of a quiet, bitter argument. He listened. George wanted the big balls hung on the little tree.

He insisted they were the best ones. Kathy said heatedly the tree was too little. You had to use the little stuff.

"Not even the birds or the sled?"

"Sleigh, not sled. It's too big."

"But it's *always* been there."

"Knock it off, you two," Ben said. "Put the little stuff on the tree. George, you can pick the bigger things you want and put those on the mantel."

"You fix the tree," George said to his sister. "*I'll* fix the mantel."

"Then the stuff we can't use we'll give away," Ben said. "We won't ever need it again. I can leave it at the firehouse."

An hour later he came out of his book and found that Helen was helping the kids. The mantel was thick with spruce boughs. It was as big as a bed in a hunting camp. The boughs hung over the edge. Lights had been strung along the mantel. Kathy was intently turning the little tree into a work of art. George and his mother were hanging ornaments from the boughs.

"Where'd all the greenery come from?" Ben asked.

"George did some trimming of the trees out in back."

"Way back where it won't show," George said.

Ben watched operations for several minutes. He got up and picked up a box of tinsel. "Every year I tell you, George boy. You don't put it on in great wads. You hang one strand at a time. Like this."

Helen stopped and watched him for a few moments. Kathy was softly humming "O Little Town of Bethlehem" with unfortunate traces of syncopation.

When they were through, they opened the box from Helen's mother. Ben dug out a flat box in silver paper. He looked it over and said, "As usual no tag. Why can't that woman fasten a tag on a package so it stays there?"

"They'll all be in the bottom. Anyway that's a tie, so it's yours," George said.

"You, boy, are old enough to get a tie," Ben informed him.

"I sure hope I don't," George said, shocked to the core.

Ben tapped the box against the palm of his hand and frowned. "We can't be sure. It's getting late. Let's stack the stuff. Maybe we'll open it tomorrow."

On Saturday afternoon Helen was in the kitchen when George came in. She had sent him to the supermarket for a dozen eggs. He laid the eggs down gently and then crashed another object onto the table top. It seemed to be about the size and general consistency of a harbor mine.

"What's that?" Helen asked.

"If I had a bike it could have gone in the basket part, then I wouldn'ta dropped it twice already."

"What is it?"

"Oh, it's a turkey. They give it to me."

"Gave it to me. Ben, come here, dear."

Ben had brought some work home. He came out, blue pencil in hand. "Dear, I want you to hear this. George, who gave you this enormous thing?"

"The store did. You won it. You know, writing on those cards. It's twenty-two pounds. Frozen."

Helen looked helplessly at Ben. "With every purchase of ten dollars or more, you can make out a card and drop it in a box. It's all frozen. I guess we could save it but I don't know how in the world I'd make room in the freezer."

"You get the steaks yet?"

"I was going to pick them up Monday."

Ben pulled the bird out of the bag. It was wrapped in clear plastic. "Big, isn't it?"

"It looks like a good one. Plump."

"I want a leg," George said firmly.

"Well . . ." Ben said. "This isn't our doing. Will he fit in the oven?"

"Barely."

"Okay," he said and went to work, looking back over his shoulder at the bird as he left the kitchen.

Helen pulled her stool over to the counter and started a new list. Rice, turnip, squash, cranberry sauce, onions. She made room in the freezer and stowed the bird away, giving it a little pat on the white meat.

On Sunday Ben suddenly became aware that the pile of presents on the table had grown. There was a satellite pile under the table. There seemed to be a great number of ribbons and bows, trees and reindeer. The kids were out skating. Helen was deep in the back pages of the Sunday paper.

"Say," he said with a trace of indignation, "how about this wrapping routine? Don't look so blank, honey. The presents. Remember?"

"Oh! Of course. I did most of my shopping at Wesley's. They always gift-wrap everything. I thought that if I told them to use plain paper, it would have just upset everybody. And Kathy did hers there too. And then there's some more out-of-town stuff that came. Some of the things I bought are in plain white paper, really."

She went back to the paper. Ben studied the pile for a time, and then went to the bedroom and took the things he had purchased from the top of his closet shelf. He carried them out and put them on the stack. He had written the names on the wrapping paper. He stepped back and looked at the presents. He had never realized that brown paper could look so terribly brown. He studied the pile and then made some judicious rearrangements. With the brown ones properly dispersed, with some of them tucked completely out of sight the general picture was improved. As he started to turn around, he thought he heard a suspicious rattle of paper. He looked thoughtfully at the back of the newspaper Helen was holding up.

When the kids came home, he made a bold counterstroke. He made certain he had George's full attention when he said casually, "I know how hard it is for you kids to wait. It's all right with us any time you want to dig out your own stuff and open it. Tomorrow is a holiday for nearly everybody and the next day is Christmas, so I guess we're technically in the gift-opening period."

"Okay," George said, but with a curious listlessness. He drifted around the presents, poking, sniffing and rattling in a rather half-hearted way. Then he disappeared. When he came back he had a small stack of presents, clumsily and earnestly gift-wrapped.

"Where did you get the gift paper, boy?" Ben asked.

"From her," George said.

"Don't call her her."

"From Mom."

"It was left over, dear. I had to wrap the out-of-town presents. They wouldn't understand our new policy. And you can't make it come out even."

"You sure had a lot left over."

"Well, you certainly can't wrap everything in the same pattern, can you?"

George apparently felt an obligation. He dug around and found one for himself that was quite obviously a book. He opened it and said heartily, "Gee, this is swell. Thanks, Mom"

"Going to open some more?"

"I kinda guess I'll go read this first. Okay?"

"Sure."

They had all the presents on Christmas morning. Ben knew that love and thought had gone into the selection of the things for him. And in expressing his appreciation he inserted the idea that it was the gift itself, not the fancy wrappings, that was the important thing. He felt uneasy every time anyone

18

unwrapped one of the brown-paper jobs and he was glad when the last one was opened. He was so intent on that he made a serious oversight. He looked at his son and wondered what on earth had happened to him. George sat on the floor with his presents. He wore a grin so artificial that it looked as though he were keeping his mouth spread by hooking his fingers in the corners. His eyes were wide, glassy and despairing. It took Ben three seconds to realize what was the matter.

"George, kindly wipe that horrid grin off your face. Then go and put on your jacket and go to the Conroys' house and ask them politely if you can wheel a certain object that belongs to you out of their garage."

George became a blur of movement, disappearing with such speed that Ben felt he should have left the hideous grin behind to fade slowly away à la Cheshire cat.

It was nearly midnight on Christmas night when Ben eased out into the kitchen and hacked a slab of white meat off the large but mortally wounded turkey. The kids had gone to bed. He strolled restlessly around the living room. Helen was making another inventory of her presents and looked as if she might purr.

She looked up at Ben. He was flipping through the records. "A nice new-fashioned Christmas," she said.

He spun sharply, then grinned in a shamefaced way. "A fine thing! Sometimes you get a real ironic tone on you, toots. So it came out the same."

"Almost the same. When you have an established routine— a good routine—don't you feel a little queer when just one thing is left out? I mean if it were entirely different . . ."

Ben sighed and took out the record, showed her the front of the jacket.

"Kids?" she asked.

"Wake 'em up."

So with only the lights of the wreaths and the tree they lis-

19

tened again to an old and timeless magic, and the chains rattled and there was the hollow voice of Christmas Past, and the kids sighed with satisfaction when it was over. They went back to bed. Ben sat with his wife on the couch. He got up and went over and snaked a piece of overlooked red ribbon from under the chair. He scooped an indignant Twombley away from dreams of mice. Twombley stood, shoulders hunched in awkward, icy, feline dignity, while Ben tied a bow in the red ribbon. Helen adjusted the bow. Twombley stalked away, scratched impotently under the chin, turned and gave them an arctic glare, found the spot on the rug he wanted and tumbled back into sleep.

"Humbug," Benjamin West said.

"Bah," said Helen beside him. He looked down and saw the tree lights in her dark eyes and saw that she was to be kissed, which was about the best way to say what he had to say.

"Here come the ornaments!"

The dreadful fate that
overtook a rash youth
who told those who
know better,
"There isn't any Santa Claus!"

By Ogden Nash

THE BOY WHO LAUGHED
AT SANTA CLAUS

In Baltimore there lived a boy.
He wasn't anybody's joy.
Although his name was Jabez Dawes,
His character was full of flaws.
In school he never led his classes,
He hid old ladies' reading glasses,
His mouth was open when he chewed,
And elbows to the table glued.
He stole the milk of hungry kittens,
And walked through doors marked
  NO ADMITTANCE.
He said he acted thus because
There wasn't any Santa Claus.
Another trick that tickled Jabez
Was crying "Boo!" at little babies.
He brushed his teeth, they said in town,
Sideways instead of up and down.

Yet people pardoned every sin,
And viewed his antics with a grin,

23

Till they were told by Jabez Dawes,
"There isn't any Santa Claus!"
Deploring how he did behave,
His parents swiftly sought their grave.
They hurried through the portals pearly,
And Jabez left the funeral early.

Like whooping cough, from child to child,
He sped to spread the rumor wild:
"Sure as my name is Jabez Dawes
There isn't any Santa Claus!"
Slunk like a weasel or a marten
Through nursery and kindergarten,
Whispering low to every tot,
"There isn't any, no there's not!"

The children wept all Christmas Eve
And Jabez chortled up his sleeve.
No infant dared hang up his stocking
For fear of Jabez' ribald mocking.
He sprawled on his untidy bed,
Fresh malice dancing in his head,
When presently with scalp a-tingling,
Jabez heard a distant jingling;
He heard the crunch of sleigh and hoof
Crisply alighting on the roof.

What good to rise and bar the door?
A shower of soot was on the floor.
What was beheld by Jabez Dawes?
The fireplace full of Santa Claus!
Then Jabez fell upon his knees
With cries of "Don't," and "Pretty please."

He howled, "I don't know where you read it,
But anyhow, I never said it!"

"Jabez," replied the angry saint,
"It isn't I, it's you that ain't.
Although there is a Santa Claus,
There isn't any Jabez Dawes!"
Said Jabez then with impudent vim,
"Oh, yes there is; and I am him!
Your magic don't scare me, it doesn't"—
And suddenly he found he wasn't!

From grimy feet to grimy socks,
Jabez became a Jack-in-the-box,
An ugly toy with springs unsprung,
Forever sticking out his tongue.
The neighbors heard his mournful squeal;
They searched for him, but not with zeal.
No trace was found of Jabez Dawes,
Which led to thunderous applause,
And people drank a loving cup
And went and hung their stockings up.

All you who sneer at Santa Claus,
Beware the fate of Jabez Dawes,
The saucy boy who mocked the saint.
Donder and Blitzen licked off his paint.

It was Christmas day,
and a twelve-year-old boy
had nothing to give his
five little brothers and sisters—
except a new home for each.

By *Dale Eunson*

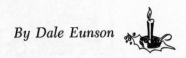

Illustrated by
Fritz Kredel

THE DAY THEY GAVE BABIES AWAY

I SUPPOSE you don't remember your grand-
father at all, Joan. For the few years he lived after you were
born we were in New York and he in California. You saw him
only once, that summer we drove west when you were four
years old. He thought you were pretty wonderful. Which was
right in character since he thought all his children and his
grandchildren were better than anybody else's.

I have a very precious mental picture of you sitting on his
lap—he was eighty-three then, still handsome, his hair silvery
white, his features still rugged and strong, his black eyes
dimmed a little by the memories and the confusions of things
they had seen. And of course it is a moving picture because
he is talking, spinning yarns he has spun for three-quarters of
a century, telling tales of his boyhood, his young manhood, tales
he had told me when I was your age and older. About the
bear he met face to face in the Wisconsin woods the fall he was
twelve—about the time he had all his teeth pulled by an itiner-
ant dentist in the town square with the simple anaesthesia of
a pint of rye whiskey—about the time when he was sheriff of
Clark County and brought in an insane killer single-handed.

27

You liked the stories, I remember, which was natural because dozens of children had liked them before you. And you loved him. I'm glad of that because he was a very remarkable fellow. You see, he'd had to be in order to survive at all.

So now, on this Christmas, in the age of the atom and jet planes and television, the era of inflation and jitters, the time when the soul of man is once more being tried and found in too many instances a little smaller than life, I want to go way back and tell you about another Christmas seventy-eight years ago when your grandfather was twelve years old, just the age you are now.

Your great grandfather was a sailor and a shipbuilder. His name was Robert Strong Eunson and, though I have never been there, I understand the name is as common in the Orkney and Shetland Islands as Smith and Jones in America. Robert Strong married in 1855 and crossed the Atlantic with his new wife Mamie during the spring of '56. There is no record of why they came. I can only assume that the American dream attracted them to the New World. They seem to have headed straight for the heart of America, Chicago being the place where Robert and Mamie first stopped to catch their breath and look about them. Mamie was six months with child, and they would have to find a home quickly. Robert, who had spent most of his savings for their passage, could waste little time in finding work.

He found it in a little town on the Fox River in Wisconsin. Small boats were built there, launched into the Fox, floated down to Lake Winnebago, and thence to Green Bay on Lake Michigan.

They moved into a four-room log house near the river, only a few steps from Robert's work. Mamie could sit on the porch, if she ever had the time, and watch him in the boat yard. He could straighten up from his bench occasionally and wave to her. They were very much in love, very young and carefree. Both of them were black Scots, with black hair, black eyes, and enormous vitality.

On October 12th, in the year 1856, their first child was born. They named him Robert for his father and his father's father, and from the first he was a lusty infant whose screams could be heard, when the windows were open, clear down to the ship-yard and beyond. He was delivered by Mrs. Pugmeyer, the midwife who lived next door.

Young Robbie, as they called him, was the spit and image of his father, noisy, roistering, good hearted, quick to anger, quicker to forgive. One of the early stories concerning him is that at the age of two he got into a brawl with a three-year-old from across the street, landed a lucky haymaker and knocked the older boy galley west. The kid's name was John Bradley, and his father, a storekeeper, demanded that Robbie be kept tied up so that he would not terrorize the neighbor-hood. Finally Robert had about enough of this and swung on him. It was like son like father that time. Robert helped Mr. Bradley to his feet and apologized, but said Bradley had better keep young John out of the way because he'd be damned if he'd tie up any son of *his*. This was a free country, wasn't it?

Later that same day the Bradleys and the Eunsons looked out in the street and discovered Robbie and John playing peaceably together. And, to show there were no hard feelings, Mamie took her trade to the Bradley store.

Brothers and sisters for Robbie arrived at two-year intervals. First came Jimmie, who was a younger edition of Robbie—the same black hair and piercing black eyes, but with a slightly mellower disposition. Then there was Kirk. He didn't like to fight so Robbie always fought his battles for him. Robert thought Kirk might become a fiddler, and when he was six years old made the boy a violin himself in the shipyard. There were three girls—Annabelle, Elizabeth, and Jane, all named for Mamie's sisters back home. They seemed to repeat the pattern of the boys in disposition and character. Annabelle was quick-tempered, quick-gaited. She never walked when she could run. She was her father's child, loving, tempestuous, flirting with the boys at four, her black pigtails flying in the breeze. Elizabeth was her mother's—quieter, motherly, affectionate and protective. And Jane? She seems to have been the dreamer and romantic. Robert, who loved music, began to think of her as a pianist. He looked forward to the days when she and Kirk would make music for him and Mamie and the neighbors to dance by. (Robert was a great one for the clog and hornpipe.)

And the Eunson family prospered a little, though it was along no quick road to riches. As soon as he could, Robert stopped selling his trade by the day and went into business for himself. He began to contract for small river and lake boats, hiring other men, though he worked alongside them himself. There were good times and lean times. An injury to his shoulder kept him out of the Civil War, and the war in turn kept him from the affluence which might have been his.

Yet the family got along. The growing town pushed the forest back. Wisconsin was mostly timberland then, and it was during those years that the big loggers began to realize the fortune to be had for the mere felling and transporting of the tall maples and spruce and pine to the sawmills that mushroomed along the rivers and lakes. Winters when the waterways were solid, the frozen stillness of the forest was shattered by the rasp of the saw, the ring of the ax, and the crashing of the giants. And when the ice broke up, the rivers were clogged with the logs, dead and stripped of their limbs, rushing over the rapids, jamming the narrows, piling up before the dam sluice gates, there to be herded through for final disposition as siding, floors, supports, matches, furniture, fuel.

The Fox, idling through the Eunson's front yard, was one of these rivers. In winter Robbie and his brother, Jim, would skate on it. They had to take turns, because there was only one pair of skates, but these were beauties which turned up at the toes and supported tiny bells that made music with each stride across the ice.

That was Robbie's world for twelve years, physically a small world but an ever exciting one, emotionally a world made warm and full by the love which he received and gave back doubled to his family and his friends.

In the summer of 1868 Kirk came down with diphtheria. Robert had a friend who owned a log cabin up in the woods, and Mamie said the only thing was for him to take the other five to the cabin and stay there with them until Kirk got well.

So Robbie and Jimmie and their three small sisters took to the woods with their father. For the girls it was all adventure, berrying in the underbrush, spotting a speckled faun, finding strange and wonderful flowers, listening at night to the not so very distant cries of wild animals, shivering and drawing close to each other trying to guess what they were, hearing a bear prowl outside the cabin, watching the moon through the window as it crawled up and up the branches of the trees.

But for Robbie and Jimmie the adventure was clouded by

When she went out of her head, he took the responsibility upon himself. There was no money, but Dr. Delbert did not mind that.

After he had seen her he called young Bob outside and told him what was the trouble. "Your mamma is a very sick woman," he said. "Do you understand?"

Bob said, "You mean she might not get well?"

"Well," Dr. Delbert said, "we can always hope. But I want you to come a-running if there's any change. I'll be here every morning and every night to see her. But in the meantime you'd better get Mrs. Pugmeyer to come in and take over."

"She's gone," Bob said. "She's down to Omro visiting her daughter until after New Year's."

"You ought to have somebody," the doctor said.

"We'll get along," Bob said. "I'll stay home from school."

"You're a good lad," the doctor said, sighed and patted him on the back. "Mrs. Delbert will be over every now and then to look in on you."

Mamie grew worse—and better—and worse. She was delirious most of the time, but there were periods of lucidity. These must have been harrowing to her, for whenever she was herself the six children crowded into the room to say Hello to Mamma. On the morning of the 23rd, and after the brood had flocked out, she asked young Bob to remain.

She took his hand in hers. It was hot and dry and her eyes were fierce. He had to bend close to hear her. She told him she was going to die. She knew it. She said not to feel bad for her, not to mourn her because there wouldn't be time. And then she told him what he was to do with the children. They were all nice, good children, she said, and he could get decent homes for them. Since the responsibility must be his, he was to decide where they were to be offered.

Bob couldn't speak, but she had to know he understood so she made him nod his head after each point.

"You watch out for them," she said. "You go and see to it as often as you can that they're taken care of."

He nodded his head.

And then she said, "Robbie, you get a good place for yourself. Promise me."

She let go of his hand and began once more to mumble unintelligibly, and he fled from the room and ran out into the woodshed.

Mamie died later that day.

After the funeral next day Dr. and Mrs. Delbert and Mr. and Mrs. Bradley came back to the empty Eunson house with the children. They felt, with justification perhaps, that they were the town's most substantial and solid citizens amongst the friends of the Eunson family. The problem was, What to Do with the Children, and it could not be put off.

Kirk, and Annabelle and Elizabeth and Jane were sent outside to play while Bob and Jimmie, who was ten, sat around the stove in the kitchen with the Delberts and Bradleys. Dr. Delbert spoke first.

"You children will have to be put out for adoption," he said, "and I'm afraid we can't expect any one family to take on six youngsters."

Mrs. Delbert and Mrs. Bradley were dabbing at their eyes with their handkerchiefs, and muttering "Poor little tykes, poor little motherless young uns." Bob was dry-eyed, though his throat was full and he could not yet speak.

"Six is a lot," Mr. Bradley said. "Maybe the Owenses would take two. Faith and I could take on Robert in a pinch, I guess."

Mrs. Delbert said, "Our family's so large already . . ."

Young Bob found his voice then. "You all mean to be kind, I guess, but I'm the oldest one and Mamma said I was to decide where we were to go."

"You?" Dr. Delbert was naturally surprised.

"That's right," Bob said, not quite daring to meet the man's eyes. "And there's something I'd like. Tomorrow's Christmas. It'll probably be our last chance to be together on Christmas. Would you please go away now and leave us alone? And day after tomorrow we can make up our minds?"

The Delberts and the Bradleys looked at each other, and they seemed about to protest when Jimmie spoke up. "That's not very much to ask, is it?"

Dr. Delbert cleared his throat. "No, you're right, James. That's not very much to ask. Coming, Edith?"

So they left the children alone that night. There was plenty of food in the house, and after supper they huddled together. There were no Christmas stories, no presents, which was odd, but perhaps the townspeople thought it would be not quite proper to give presents to children who had just been orphaned. Bob put the younger ones to sleep by telling them stories about Scotland and the days when Robert and Mamie were young, and how the young couple had come to America so that their children—Robert and James and Kirk and Annabelle and Elizabeth and Jane—would have a better chance. It was big talk for a twelve-year-old, much too big talk for the younger ones, but somehow he had to tell it while they were all together. He had to let them know that they were still going to have that chance.

So finally, one by one, their heads nodded and they went to sleep, and only Bob and Jimmie were awake. They talked until midnight, and they made a list on a paper bag, a list of the families of the town that they thought would like children, be good to them and bring them up as they would their own.

"We won't wait until day after tomorrow," Bob said.

"But you told Dr. Delbert you would," Jimmie said.

"I know that. But Mamma told me *I* was to decide. They won't let me. And tomorrow being Christmas . . ."

Mr. Howard Tyler owned the livery stable. He had twelve

horses, four teamsters and half a dozen rigs. He was, as they said in those days, well fixed. Bob had spent many hours at his stable, for he loved horses, and sometimes Mr. Tyler let him pump water into the troughs. Mrs. Tyler, already the mother of two boys, Howard, Jr. and Bruce, was a leader in church doings and a great organizer.

The Tylers were ready to enjoy their Christmas dinner at one that afternoon. Mr. Tyler had just lifted his head from saying grace when there come a rather timid knock on the kitchen door. Mrs. Tyler frowned, said, "Now who could that be? Everybody should be at home enjoying their victuals this time of day," and went to the door. Two small children greeted her, a boy of twelve and a girl of six. She immediately recognized them as Eunson children.

"Why, Bobby," she said, "I thought you'd be with the Bradleys or the Delberts. Come in, come in."

She noticed as she held the door for them that they both looked scrubbed and shining and were dressed in their Sunday best. The girl's hair was plaited and tied with two red bows that were not quite the same color as her stocking cap.

By this time they were in the dining room. The two boys stared at the visitors, but Mr. Tyler got to his feet and shook hands with Bob. "You'll have Christmas dinner with us," he said. "And don't argue. We won't take No, will we, Emma?"

"Begging your pardon, but I was wondering—that is Jimmie and I were wondering—if you didn't need a, a sort of sister, for Howie and Bruce. Annabelle here is a good little girl, and she'd be an awful help to you. She's—that is she *was*—learning to sew and she can wipe dishes and she knows her ABC's."

"A-b-c-d-e-f-g-h-" Annabelle began.

Mrs. Tyler's mouth started to work in a very strange sort of way. Mr. Tylter coughed and turned his head. Howie, who was six, stared at Annabelle and said, "What you got in that bundle?"

"I-j-k-l . . . My clothes," Annabelle said. "M-n-o-p- . . ."

And then Mrs. Tyler had grasped her husband's hand and was staring into his eyes. "Howard," she said. "It's Christmas. We've got to—we've wanted a girl."

"Mamma always said Annabelle was a good helper," Bob put in.

And then for some reason Mr. Tyler kissed Mrs. Tyler right there before them all, and when he let her go she turned away and blew her nose while Mr. Tyler squatted down and took hold of Annabelle's shoulders. "Do you think you're going to like living at our house?" he asked. He was already unbuttoning her coat.

She did not answer because she was working on her overshoes, but Bob said, "Yes, Mr. Tyler. She'll like it a lot."

"We'll be good to her, Bobby," he said. "I guess you and I know each other."

"I know you, Mr. Tyler," Bob said.

And so Annabelle was accounted for. Hereafter she would be Annabelle Tyler. She would live in comparative luxury, for the Tylers were to prosper and become important citizens of the state. But as young Bob left her there that Christmas day all he could be sure of was that she would be well loved. And that was enough.

Meanwhile, Jimmie, leaving Kirk home to take care of baby Jane, had hauled Elizabeth on his green sled to the Potters' house across the river. But the Potters were gone for the day, so it happened that Bob ran into his brother and sister on the all but deserted Main Street. Elizabeth was cold and fretful and her nose was running. The boys had not provided themselves with any alternate foster parents the night before, and so Elizabeth, whimpering there on the sled, suddenly assumed the characteristics of a white elephant, a very dear but vexing one.

"What'll we do?" Jimmie asked. "She's getting blue. We can't keep her out much longer." And then his face brightened a little. "There's the Carters. They live close."

"He owns a saloon," Bob said. "Mamma would hate that."

They agreed that this was so, and began walking aimlessly down the street and around the block. As long as they kept moving, Elizabeth was quiet. One would mention a name, only to have the other boy discard it. Then they saw a cutter with two fast bays trotting toward them down the street. The boys looked at each other and nodded. Bobby ran out in the street waving his arms.

The horses came to a stop, blowing steam from their nostrils, pawing the snow. Inside the cutter, wrapped in a coonskin lap robe were a middle-aged man and woman.

"Hello, Mr. and Mrs. Stevens," Bob said. "I was just coming to see you."

"You were?" the man said. "Mrs. Stevens and I have been over at your house. We wanted to see if there was anything we could do."

"There is," Bob said. "That is, it's quite a lot to ask, but I thought since you and Mrs. Stevens didn't have any children you might like to take Elizabeth. That's her," he said pointing.

39

"That is *she*," Mr. Stevens corrected. He was the principal of the school.

"*Take* her," Mrs. Stevens said. "You mean—?"

"Well, sort of—sort of adopt her. She's bright. She doesn't look very pretty now, but you'd learn to like her. Mamma and papa did. Mamma never had any favorites, but if she had any, I guess Elizabeth would have been the one. She's quiet."

It happened that Mrs. Stevens had never been able to produce a child for her husband. They never talked about it, but she was afraid she had been a great disappointment to him. He called his pupils "My children" but, having none of his own, was inclined to be pompous with them, and held them at a distance. The truth was that he was afraid to show how much he liked and needed them. Even now he did not let his eyes go to Elizabeth, but turned them to his wife. When he spoke, his voice was almost stern.

"You wouldn't care to take on this burden, would you, Jess?"

"Wouldn't I just!" And with a bound she was out of the cutter and had swooped Elizabeth into her arms.

When they got home it was about two-thirty. Kirk met them at the door with a wild look on his face. "Old Mrs. Runyon's in there," he whispered. "Says she's going to take Jane."

Now here was a problem. Old Mrs. Runyon had been a widow for twenty years. She wore nothing but black and carried a cane that she used to swipe at dogs that nipped at her heels. She had once crippled a collie pup and it had had to be put away. So with some justification, perhaps, she had evolved into a town character used as a threat to frighten children into obedience. As long as Bob and Jimmie could remember they'd heard the expression, "You better be good or ol' Runyon will get you."

And now here she was to "get" Jane. It must have taken no little courage for Bob to face her.

When he walked into the house she had Jane on her lap. He said, "I'm sorry, Mrs. Runyon, but Jane's already promised."

"Who to?" she snapped.

He floundered then. He and Jimmie had the Ellises, a young couple with a baby girl, in mind for Jane, but of course the Ellises had not yet been consulted. So he said, "Nobody you know."

"I know everybody in this town," Mrs. Runyon said.

"These folks don't live in this town." Bob said the first thing that came into his head. "They're—they're way up in Berlin."

"I don't believe you," the old woman said. "Besides, by whose authority are these children being disposed of?"

"Mamma said I was to decide," Bob said, standing his ground.

"You! Why you're just a little boy. We'll see about this."

With that she put Jane back in her crib, and marched out of the house swinging her cane. They didn't know what Mrs. Runyon might do, but they felt that they hadn't much time to finish the job.

"You take Kirk over to the Cramers," Bob told Jimmie. The Cramers had no children, but Mrs. Cramer did own a 'cello which she was said to play very nicely. "Tell them Kirk can fiddle pretty good."

Kirk had begun to cry. "I don't want to go," he said. "I want to stay with you."

Bob had been afraid of this. Kirk was the soft one. So Bob thrust his fiddle into Kirk's arms and gave him a shove. "Get a move on, and don't be a cry baby. Annabelle and Elizabeth didn't cry. Who do you think you are?"

He pushed Kirk away from him and Jimmie took him by the hand and led him out the door. He stood there in the middle of the room and for a minute the weight of what he was doing was too heavy for him. His knees collapsed under him and he sat down on the floor and beat it with his fists until they hurt and brought him to his senses. Then he got up and as fast as he could changed all of Jane's clothes and shook her into sweater, leggings and coat. She was delighted at the prospect of going somewhere, and made no trouble. And before he was finished Jimmie came back.

"Did they take him?" Bob asked.

Jimmie nodded. "What are you going to do with Janey?" he asked.

"Take her up to Berlin."

"But that's twelve miles."

"I'll pull her up the river on our skates, and then bring them back to you—sometime."

"You going to stay up there?" Jimmie asked.

"I'm going to work," Bob said. "Rounds's camp is just five miles out of town."

"You can have the skates," Jimmie said after a moment. "The skates and my sled for your red sled. Fair enough?"

The red sled had been Bob's pride, but where he was going he would not have much use for a boy's sled. So he said, "Fair enough." And then, "You talked to the Raidens?"

"No," Jimmie said. "But I don't have to. They'll take me in.

42

You know Mrs. Raiden's always said she wished she had a boy like me."

Yet there was something in Jimmie's voice that betrayed a slight distaste for the Raidens, and Bob heard it. "You like 'em all right, don't you?" he asked.

"I like 'em all right," he admitted.

"Then what's the matter?"

"All those girls!" Jimmie said. The Raidens had four daughters aged from twelve to seven. "I can just hear them." His little boy voice went into a ridiculous imitation of a falsetto. "This is our new brother, Jimmie. Ain't he cute?"

"Well, ain't you?" Bob said.

Then Jimmie swung on him, and caught him on the jaw. Bob was stunned, but fought back while Jane looked on in wide-eyed excitement and approval. They tussled, grappled, and struck at each other until the room was a shambles and Bob had pinned Jimmie to the floor.

"Admit you're cute?"

"I'm cute," Jimmie gagged.

They both got up and straightened their clothes. They didn't know why they had fought, but they were glad they had. It had cleared the atmosphere. Somehow they were small boys again, small boys who had fought for a reason that small boys fight. It had momentarily eased the burden.

And soon, all too soon, they were standing outside with Jane strapped to the green sled. This was the moment Bob had dreaded. He was afraid Jimmie would want to kiss him Goodbye, but the younger boy seemed to realize this was not the thing to do. So they stood looking at Jane, not daring to look at each other. And then Bob said, "You go first."

"You'll skate down once in a while?" Jimmie asked.

"Sure," Bob said. "Every chance I get. And see you don't start wearing dresses with all those girls around."

"You shut up!" Jimmie said.

43

And with that he turned and, pulling the bright red sled, trudged away. Bob was afraid Jimmie might look back and see him, so he pulled Jane's sled behind the woodshed and peered out around the corner as his brother's figure grew smaller and smaller, and finally disappeared beneath the Gatesons' green picket fence.

As soon as he was strong enough, Bob went down to the river and put on his skates.

Part of the way Jane slept, lulled by the motion of the sled. Once she cried, and he stopped and held her, wiping her cheeks and nose with the red mittens Mamie had knitted for him. And when she was quiet again he put her back on the sled and tucked the blanket about her. And slowly, mile after mile, the leafless trees slid past. Then it was dark and the woods held shadows that seemed to move as Bob moved, so that for the last few miles he kept his eyes straight ahead while his legs pumped steadily and the exertion kept him warm. And each push removed them that much from the menace of old Mrs. Runyon.

At last there were feeble lights in a group of houses along the river. They passed the inevitable sawmill, skated through a group of town skaters who scarcely paused to notice the small boy and the baby on his sled. And a moment later he saw a house with Christmas tree candles winking at the front window. He came to a stop before it and gave it silent inspection. Since there was a tree there would be children, he thought. The house was not so very large. The people who lived there would not have a great deal of money. Therefore, his thoughts ran, it would be a small sacrifice to have a tree with candles. They must love their children.

So he removed his skates, took the sleeping Jane in his arms, climbed the steps onto the porch and knocked at the door.

A plump woman with a green shawl over her shoulders, and with dark hair gathered in a knot low on her neck opened the door. Instantly three children were peering around her skirts. Bob heard her say, as if from a distance, "Well, for mercy's sakes."

He said, "Please, ma'am, I wonder if you'd like to have a baby."

"I'm ashamed to say it," your grandfather used to say when he told me this story, "but I fainted. Yes sir, plumb fainted dead away."

Yes, Joan, that was what your grandfather did that Christmas when he was twelve years old. And when Jane was safe in the hands of the Clareys he said Goodbye and walked up to the Rounds camp in the woods where he became a helper, later a logger in his own right.

He always kept tabs on his brothers and sisters who mostly turned out remarkably well, though as each grew up he took on the characteristics and absorbed the points of view of his foster parents. They are all dead now, but I saw them all but one and they were alike in looks as peas in a pod. There was always something poignant to me in their love for each other, because they had nothing but that love in common. When I knew Aunt Annabelle she had become a great dowager with a home in California and one in Chicago. She ruled her children with an iron hand. Aunt Elizabeth indeed taught school, then married, had two children and, after her husband died, became the house mother at a girls' school.

Jane never married. She gave music lessons—voice—and herself possessed a sweet, small contralto. She, of course, had no memory of that evening's ride on the sled to her new home, but she and papa were always very close. She used to come to our house when I was small, and I can remember her sitting at the piano singing "In the Gloaming," and then breaking into "The Irish Washerwoman," and papa would leap to his feet with a real hoedown and make the furniture jump.

Uncle Jim became a successful lawyer in Wisconsin, married and had three children. He and papa used to write each other regularly once a month until he died twenty years ago.

Kirk was the only tragedy amongst the six. Life was too much of a struggle for him and he "took to drink," as papa used to say and died mysteriously when he was only twenty-five.

And that's about the end of the story except for your grandfather. His life, at least in his own estimation, was a happy one. He worked until he was almost eighty. He married twice, had seven children. He knew poverty and success. It was a life of ups and downs, but in the downs he used to say, "They can't lick a tough old nut like me."

They never did. Nobody ever did.

"No, no! I mean your *real* name!"

The daughter of Hugh Lofting, author of the be-loved Dr. Doolittle *books, tells how the man whose stories brought magic to thousands of children gave his own two children a special gift of believing wonder one Christmas long ago.*

By Lynne Lofting

THE NIGHT WE TALKED TO SANTA CLAUS

DURING the First World War my brother Colin and I lived with my mother in the Catskill Mountains. Our house was perched on a raised plateau, surrounded by apple trees and commanding a beautiful view of the valley and the range of mountains opposite. My mother was not with us very much; she joined the Red Cross and went overseas so that she could be near my father, who was a captain in the Irish Guards. It was at this time that we received the many illustrated letters from him about a kind, little round-faced doctor who could understand and speak to animals—letters that later became the first *Doctor Dolittle* book. The doctor and his animal friends were drawn on any old scraps of paper while my father was actually in the trenches.

I remembered my father only dimly. One evening he had carried me through the garden, perched on his shoulders, and had shown me the faint speck of light that was the evening star. He told me that it was "our" star and that wherever he was when he left us, he would be looking at it and thinking of us at home.

Wars are remote to children. The months slipped past in our mountain retreat and suddenly it was just before Christmas.

49

Our English Nanny appeared to be strangely excited. It seemed that soon, perhaps even in time for the holidays, Father and Mother would be home.

Happily forgotten in the excitement, my brother and I spent long hours in our nursery, curled up on the window seat, speculating on what we wanted most for Christmas. He was four years old and longed desperately for a real toolbox. My heart was set on a coral ring. We described these to each other in such minute detail that we had almost conjured them up before our eyes.

I can still smell the gingerbread cookies baking downstairs and taste the tang of cold air as it came in our window, blowing the curtains back suddenly to reveal the sky alive with stars. In this hushed, waiting atmosphere we stopped fighting with each other, no longer played tricks on Nanny and became model children.

At last it was Christmas Eve. But no one had arrived and the house was oddly empty and unpromising. After supper we were allowed downstairs just long enough to hang up our stockings by the fireplace. It wasn't very gay with only ourselves and Nanny there to celebrate. Disappointed and forlorn, we dragged our feet back up the stairs, getting little staccato prods in the back as Nanny hurried us up. She tucked us in and opened the window wide; she was one who believed in plenty of good fresh air. Then she came over and gave a kiss and a hug to each of us.

"Be good children and sleep tight," she said as she left the room.

The faint smell of cookies still floated about in the hall as she opened the door to leave us, but aside from that it might have been any ordinary winter night.

For a while we stayed perfectly still, each thinking his own thoughts. Soon I was sure my brother had fallen asleep. I lay looking at the sky, where a moon the color of tin was suspended like a Christmas tree ornament. It made matters worse to feel so lonesome on such a special, beautiful night. I wished that my mother were there. My eyelids grew heavy. Despite the disappointment sleep was overtaking me.

Then suddenly I heard the sound of bells—sharp, clear bells, coming closer all the time. No other sound had ever been so real; it could not be that I imagined them. I lay stiff as a poker with my legs straight out and my heart going like a hammer. My brother's muffled voice barely reached me. "Are you awake?" he whispered.

"Yes."

"Do you hear anything?"

"I hear bells," I said.

"So do I!" In one leap we were up on the window seat, our heads thrust out into the cold, sharp air, our toes curled under us in excitement, our trembling bodies pressed close together, as we tried to peer through the dark orchard down into the valley. Now we could hear the squeak of runners in the snow and the thud of hoofs.

Suddenly the moon came from behind a cloud and painted all the landscape silver. In the silence of that snow-covered world a deep voice shouted, "Who-oa Prancer! Who-oa Donder! Who-oa Blitzen!" But no one was visible.

The sleigh finally halted somewhere behind the trees that surrounded the house. There was a brief, suspended quiet. Then there were other sounds—human footsteps in the snow, crunching, coming closer to the house. And then a fat, bouncy figure with an enormous pack on his back walked toward us beneath the branches of an apple tree.

"It's Santa!" my brother squealed, butting me in the stomach with his head. "And he'll be in our chimlee in a minute!"

"Quick! We're supposed to be in bed!" With that, my brother in a desperate effort to hide himself tried to get under his, while I hurled myself into mine and pulled the covers tightly around me like a winding sheet. In this state we waited breathlessly, while the steps, in the house now, came closer and closer to the nursery door.

Slowly and with ceremony the door opened and then everything happened very quickly.

He came over to me first. I somehow gathered strength to put my head out from under the covers. He was near enough to touch. There were black streaks of soot about the hips and shoulders of his red suit. He put the enormous, bulging pack of toys down on the foot of my bed. Then he actually spoke to me. His great, booming voice came through a flowing beard which was white as snow and covered part of his chest.

"I hear you have been a very good little girl." He was reaching down into the pack of toys as he spoke. "So I brought you your wish." With that he handed me a tiny, beautifully wrapped package. I knew instinctively that it was my coral ring. I was so overwhelmed that my eyes swam with tears.

"Don't be afraid," he said with such love and kindness that I began to feel I knew him. "Take it—it's what you have wished for." I reached out and took it from him, unable to say a word.

Then he turned toward the other bed. My brother had covered his small face with his hands and peered through his chubby fingers now and then, when his courage allowed him to.

"I hear that you have been very good as well, so I have a special present for you."

My brother seemed frozen but he took one hand away from his face and eyed the jolly stranger. Santa walked over and put the square, impressive box down beside him. For a second he looked as if he might be going to pick my brother up in his arms, but then he turned away. Slowly he shouldered his pack and started for the door.

"Good night," he said. "I still have a lot to do. Merry Christmas to all and to all a good night." With that he was gone.

The silence was broken by my brother who had finally found his voice:

"If he gets stuck in the chimlee, we can see him in the morning."

"He won't," I replied sharply. Two years older and wiser, I knew that such a thing could never happen.

Dazed, we moved forward again to look out the window. We heard the same steps in the snow, but this time we didn't see anyone. We heard the bells as the reindeer started up. The sleigh moved away swiftly, down, down into the dark below. Then the night was again quite empty of sound, except for our breathing. Santa might never have been there at all.

The sleep we eventually got was deep and peaceful. In the morning Nanny came in looking just as she always did. We sprang out of bed both talking at once, showing her our treasures. She received the news with just the right mixture of belief and incredulity. When she could get a word in, she said, "Well, get your clothes on now. There's a surprise downstairs for you. Your mother *and* your father are waiting in the living room."

We raced down the stairs. Next to Mother stood a tall man with smiling eyes which were at once sad and happy. He took us in his arms and hugged us very tight. I don't remember if he said anything to us because we were too busy telling him over and over again the story of what had happened. How just when we thought there would be no Christmas, Santa Claus had come, we'd seen him in our room, he'd talked to us, he'd given me my coral ring and my brother his tool chest, and then he went away because he had a lot to do and other children to visit. Then, quite out of breath, we told it all over again.

My father listened intensely, as though every detail of what we were saying was something he longed to hear. It seemed to give him so much joy that the telling of our adventure was as tinglingly alive as the experience itself.

53

Even when we were a great deal older, we still were telling other children that we *knew* there was a Santa Claus. Our conviction remained unshaken because we had seen him and spoken to him. Against any and all assaults we stood our ground.

Later, of course, we grew to know the man who had come to our room that Christmas Eve and to understand why he had made us believe in Santa Claus. We understood why, after spending three years at war, he had come back to his children at Christmas time with one purpose in his mind and heart: to keep the magic in the world alive.

That magic was the real gift he gave us on Christmas Eve so long ago. And my brother and I cherish it still.

"It's for a man who has everything."

"If I can't have a pony, give me nothing, nothing!"
he said.

But was it possible that Santa Claus had taken him
seriously and passed him by completely?

By *Lincoln Steffens*

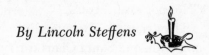

A MISERABLE MERRY CHRISTMAS

WHAT interested me in our new neighborhood was not the school, nor the room I was to have in the house all to myself, but the stable which was built back of the house. My father let me direct the making of a stall, a little smaller than the other stalls, for my pony, and I prayed and hoped that my sister Lou believed that that meant that I would get the pony, perhaps for Christmas. I pointed out to her that there were three other stalls and no horses at all. This I said in order that she should answer it. She could not. My father, sounded, said that some day we might have horses and a cow; meantime a stable added to the value of a house. "Some day" is a pain to a boy who lives in and knows only "now." My good little sisters, to comfort me, remarked that Christmas was coming and grown-ups were always talking about it, and asking you what you wanted and then giving you what they wanted you to have. Though everybody knew what I wanted, I told them all again. My mother knew that I told God, too, every night. I wanted a pony, and to make sure they understood, I declared that I wanted nothing else.

"Nothing but a pony?" my father asked.

"Nothing," I said.

"Not even a pair of high boots?"

That was hard. I did want boots, but I stuck to the pony. "No, not even boots."

"Nor candy? There ought to be something to fill your stocking with, and Santa Claus can't put a pony in a stocking."

That was true, and he couldn't lead a pony down a chimney, either. But no, "All I want is a pony," I said. "If I can't have a pony, give me nothing, nothing."

Now I had been looking myself for the pony I wanted, going to sales stables, inquiring of horsemen, and I had seen several that would do. My father let me "try" them. I tried so many ponies that I was learning fast to sit on a horse. I chose several, but my father always found some fault with them. I was in despair. When Christmas was at hand I had given up all hope of a pony, and on Christmas Eve I hung up my stocking along with my sisters'. They were so happy that I caught some of their merriment. I speculated on what I'd get; I hung up the biggest stocking I had, and we all went reluctantly to bed to wait till morning. Not to sleep; not right away. We were told that we must not only sleep promptly, we must not wake up until seven thirty the next morning—or if we did, we must not go to the fireplace for our Christmas. Impossible.

We did sleep that night, but we woke at six A.M. We lay in our beds and debated through the open doors whether to obey till, say, half-past six. Then we bolted. I don't know who started it, but there was a rush. We all disobeyed; we raced to disobey and get first to the fireplace in the front room downstairs. And there they were, the gifts, all sorts of wonderful things, mixed up piles of presents; only, as I disentangled the mess, I saw that my stocking was empty; it hung limp; not a thing in it; and under and around it—nothing.

My sisters had knelt down, each by her pile of gifts; they were squealing with delight till they looked up and saw me standing there in my nightgown with nothing. They left their piles to come to me and look with me at my empty place. Nothing. They felt my stocking: nothing.

I don't remember whether I cried at that moment, but my sisters did. They ran with me back to my bed, and there we all cried until I became indignant. That helped some. I got up, dressed, and driving my sisters away, I went alone out to the yard, down to the stable, and there, all by myself, I wept.

My mother came out to me by and by; she found me in my pony stall, sobbing on the floor, and she tried to comfort me. But I heard my father outside; he had come part way with her, and she was having some sort of angry quarrel with him. She tried to comfort me; besought me to come to breakfast. I could not; I wanted no comfort and no breakfast. She left me and went into the house with sharp words for my father.

I don't know what kind of breakfast the family had. My sisters said it was "awful." They were ashamed to enjoy their own toys. They came to me, and I was rude. I ran away from them. I went around to the front of the house, sat down on the steps, and, the crying over, I ached. I was wronged, I was hurt—I can feel now what I felt then, and I am sure that if one could see the wounds upon our hearts, there would be found still upon mine a scar from that terrible Christmas morning. And my father, the practical joker, he must have been hurt, too, a little. I saw him looking out of the window. He was watching me or something for an hour or two, drawing back the curtain ever so little lest I catch him, but I saw his face, and I think I can see now the anxiety upon it, the worried impatience.

After—I don't know how long—surely an hour or two—I was brought to the climax of my agony by the sight of a man riding a pony down the street, a pony and a brand-new saddle; the most beautiful saddle I ever saw, and it was a boy's saddle. The man's feet were not in the stirrups; his legs were too long. The outfit was perfect; it was the realization of all of my dreams, the answer to all of my prayers. A fine new bridle, with a light curb bit. And the pony! As he drew near, I saw that the pony was really a small horse, what we called an Indian pony, a bay, with black mane and tail, and one white foot and a white star on his forehead. For such a horse as that I would have given, I could have forgiven, anything.

But the man, a disheveled fellow with a blackened eye and a fresh-cut face, came along, reading the numbers of the houses, and, as my hopes—my impossible hopes—rose, he looked at our door and passed by, he and the pony, and the saddle and the bridle. Too much. I fell upon the steps, and, having wept before, I broke now into such a flood of tears that I was a floating wreck when I heard a voice.

"Say, kid," it said, "do you know a boy named Lennie Steffens?" I looked up. It was the man on the pony, back again, at our horse block.

"Yes," I spluttered through my tears. "That's me."

"Well," he said, "then this is your horse. I've been looking all over for you and your house. Why don't you put your number where it can be seen?"

"Get down," I said, running out to him.

He went on saying something about "ought to have gotten here at seven o'clock; told me to bring the nag here and tie him to your post and leave him for you. But, hell, I got into a drunk—and a fight—and a hospital, and—"

"Get down," I said.

He got down, and he boosted me up to the saddle. He offered to fit the stirrups to me, but I didn't want him to. I wanted to ride.

"What's the matter with you?" he said angrily. "What you crying for? Don't you like the horse? He's a dandy, this horse. I know him of old. He's fine at cattle; he'll drive 'em alone."

I hardly heard, I could scarcely wait, but he persisted. He adjusted the stirrups, and then, finally, off I rode, slowly, at a

walk, so happy, so thrilled, that I did not know what I was doing. I did not look back at the house or the man. I rode off
up the street, taking note of everything—of the reins, of the
pony's long mane, of the carved leather saddle. I had never
seen anything so beautiful. And mine! I was going to ride up
past Miss Kay's house. But I noticed on the horn of the saddle
some stains like rain-drops, so I turned and trotted home, not to
the house but to the stable. There was the family, father,
mother, sisters, all working for me, all happy. They had been
putting in place the tools of my new business: blankets, curry-
comb, brush, pitchfork—everything, and there was hay in the
loft.

"What did you come back so soon for?" somebody asked.
"Why didn't you go on riding?"

I pointed to the stains. "I wasn't going to get my new saddle
rained on," I said. And my father laughed. "It isn't raining,"
he said. "Those aren't raindrops."

"They are tears," my mother gasped, and she gave my father
a look which sent him off to the house. Worse still, my mother
offered to wipe away the tears still running out of my eyes. I
gave her such a look as she had given him, and she went off
after my father, drying her own tears. My sisters remained and
we all unsaddled the pony, put on his halter, led him to his
stall, tied and fed him. It began really to rain; so all the rest
of that memorable day we curried and combed that pony. The
girls plaited his mane, forelock, and tail, while I pitchforked
hay to him and curried and brushed, curried and brushed. For
a change we brought him out to drink; we led him up and
down, blanketed like a race-horse; we took turns at that. But
the best, the most inexhaustible fun, was to clean him. When
we went reluctantly to our midday Christmas dinner, we all
smelt of horse, and my sisters had to wash their faces and
hands. I was asked to, but I wouldn't, till my mother bade me
look in the mirror. Then I washed up—quick. My face was

caked with muddy lines of tears that had coursed over my cheeks to my mouth. Having washed away that shame, I ate my dinner, and as I ate I grew hungrier and hungrier. It was my first meal that day, and as I filled up on the turkey and the stuffing, the cranberries and the pies, the fruit and the nuts— as I swelled, I could laugh. My mother said I still choked and sobbed now and then, but I laughed, too; I saw and enjoyed my sisters' presents till—I had to go out and attend to my pony, who was there, really and truly there, the promise, the beginning, of a happy double life. And—I went and looked to make sure—there was the saddle, too, and the bridle.

But that Christmas, which my father had planned so carefully, was it the best or the worst I ever knew? He often asked me that; I never could answer as a boy. I think now that it was both. It covered the whole distance from broken-hearted misery to bursting happiness—too fast. A grown-up could hardly have stood it.

New York Times, December 1, 1957

"My name is Alice—and, *please*, no more
'Alice in Wonderlands.'"

There were a dozen or more trees on the roof. The air smelled of them. Judy hopefully glanced at the tag on the tallest one. "I don't think this is it," she said. "This one has a long name on it."

At the end of the row, in a corner protected from the wind, a small tree lay against the railing, its branches tied with string. "This must be it," Judy said. She pulled it upright and it swayed toward her. The top branches touched her cheek and the scent of it filled her nostrils. She put her arms around it and held it close. "It isn't so very big," she said, defiantly, "but it's a beautiful little tree. A perfectly *beautiful* little tree. I'll carry it."

They walked back toward the elevator.

Lois was waiting for them by the door, and she looked anxious. "It's *darling*," Judy told her quickly. "It isn't small at all. There were some larger trees on the roof, but they looked scrawny. *Really*."

She carried the tree to the living room and laid it on the clean sheet that had been spread between the windows. Her hands were sticky from the sap and dark green needles clung to her sweater.

Lois's face lost its anxious look. She had slipped a smock over her dress and it gave her an efficient appearance. "I have sort of an idea," she said. "I think it might be unusual if we picked out just blue and silver ornaments and did the whole thing in blue and silver. I mean, there would be plenty of them because the tree is so much smaller."

"Not use all the ornaments!" Judy exclaimed. "You're nuts!"

"Oh," Mrs. Graves protested, "I think it would be better to use all the ornaments. We always have, and I'm fond of them."

"Really," Lois said, "you all act like a lot of reactionaries. You just won't listen to any new suggestions, *ever*."

Mr. Graves fastened the tree in its stand and cut the string

66

from the branches. "I'll tell you what," he said. "When you're eighteen, Lois, you can trim the tree the way you want it, and when Judy's eighteen, she can trim it the way she wants it. How's that?"

He walked over to the table where the Christmas-tree ornaments lay in their boxes. Deliberately he chose a red-and-gold striped ball and hung it on the tree. His action stripped the authority from Lois and her smock and lifted the apprehension from Judy's heart.

"I'm going to put the cat face on for my first one," she said.

It took them over an hour to trim the tree and arrange the crèche on strips of cotton underneath it. Judy, kneeling to set a small celluloid reindeer near a tiny pine tree, suddenly remembered last year and how Bilgy, the cat that had died last summer, had knocked the whole scene over after they had arranged it. Her eyes smarted with tears and she shook her hair over to hide her face.

"It does seem strange without one single toy," Mrs. Graves said sadly. "It really looks bare without any toys under the tree."

"Speaking of toys—" Lois stopped abruptly and giggled.

"Speaking of toys what?" Judy asked.

"Oh, nothing," Lois told her. "You're too old for toys, of course."

"When I was twelve," Mrs. Graves said, "I was still playing with dolls."

"Dolls!" Lois exclaimed. "Oh, Mother!"

"It's living in New York," Mr. Graves said. "And that fool school."

"Well, get your stockings out, girls, and let's hang them," Mrs. Graves put in hurriedly.

Lois's stocking was silk and slim, with a small foot, and Judy brought a wool knee-length sock with a darn in the toe. "Turn your back, Judy," Lois said. She slipped a small package into the toe of Judy's sock.

"Just weight them with the candlesticks," Mrs. Graves told them. "I'll fix them later."

She went to her room and came back with her arms full of packages. "No poking at these," she said.

The Cogswell chair was for Judy's things, the wing chair for Lois's, and the couch for Mr. and Mrs. Graves' presents. Until this year Judy's chair had been almost empty, as her toys had been arranged under the tree after she had gone to bed. This year her chair looked the same as Lois's. Judy, glancing at the packages, wondered if the biggest one could be the jade-green lounging pajamas.

She got the gifts for her father, mother, and Lois from the shelf in her closet. She had bought her father a gadget called a Scotch Bartender, which measured an exact jigger of whiskey, and a practical and charming present for her mother. It was an ashtray, and attached to it was a frog's head. You inserted a cigarette in a place in the mouth, and the ashes fell in the tray. A silk-covered rubber tube extended from the inside of the frog's head and ended in a dainty amber cigarette holder. The idea of the whole thing was to be able to smoke in bed without fear of dropping ashes on the blankets and perhaps going up in flames. For Lois, she had bought a pair of red gloves fastened at the back with a gilt Christmas bell. She had wrapped her packages with care and covered them with stickers that called out, "Season's Greetings," "Joyeux Noël," "Merry Christmas," or warned, "Do Not Open Until Christmas" and "Hands Off Until Dec. 25th."

Lois had wrapped her gifts in blue cellophane and tied them with silver ribbon. Her stickers were silver stars.

It was almost midnight by the time the room was straightened and the carols were sung. Activity had thawed the lump in Judy's stomach somewhat, and she was surprised to find that

68

she was a little sleepy. "I'll never close an eye," she said.

When Lois and Judy were in bed, Mrs. Graves came in to kiss them good night. "I never can realize that you two will never believe in Santa Claus again," she sighed.

"Judy pretended she did until she was almost *eight*," Lois said.

"I did not."

"I beg to differ."

Mrs. Graves uncurled Judy's fingers. "You didn't even wash."

"I did," Judy said, "all but this hand. That isn't dirt, it's sap and it smells good."

She turned on her side and snapped out the light over her bed. For almost five minutes, it seemed as though morning would never come.

The next thing Judy knew, it had come and gone in a swirl of white tissue paper, red ribbons, excited exclamations, and kisses. The big package had contained the jade-green lounging pajamas, which were a little too short and had to be exchanged. There were six pairs of silk stockings of a new shade called Woodsmoke, a pair of pink silk pants with lace edges, a silk nightgown that trailed on the floor, monogrammed writing paper, a new charm bracelet with fourteen charms on it, a bottle of 4711 eau de cologne, white kid gloves that fastened with a zipper, a tiny bottle of real perfume (lily of the valley), bedroom slippers with white fur tops, and, from Lois, a blue satin stocking box. The big present, of course, was the lounging pajamas, but the thing that Lois had tucked in the toe of her stocking was the funniest; it was a small crib with twin dolls in it, bought from the five-and-ten. The dolls were wrapped in tiny cheap blue blankets. Judy screamed with laughter when she saw it.

"That's why," Lois explained, "I very nearly died when Mother said what she did about toys last night."

"I don't wonder," Judy answered. She set the crib under

the tree. "There, Mother, that should make you feel better."

She arranged her presents carefully in her chair. "I think I'll go over and give Fuffy hers," she said. Fuffy was her best friend and lived two blocks away.

In her room, she took off her wool socks and slid her new silk stockings over her legs. They felt strange and cold, and her shoes, when she put them on, slid up and down at the heels. Although her knees were plump, the stockings wrinkled around them and she had trouble keeping them up. She put on her new white gloves, her charm bracelet, scented a clean handkerchief with a drop of the lily-of-the-valley perfume, and started toward Fuffy's house. She held the packages stiffly, as her hands were pinched in the new gloves. Halfway down the block she met Fuffy. One glance told her that Fuffy was wearing silk stockings, and though Fuffy wore her old wool mittens, Judy could see the peach-colored collar of a new blouse showing over the top of her double-breasted coat. Fuffy was also carrying a package, identical in shape with the one Judy held. She pressed it into Judy's arms. "Here," she said. "Merry Christmas."

"Same to you," Judy replied. "And here."

They walked toward the corner and stood by a large metal basket, into which they carefully threw the tissue-paper wrappings. "I got yours green," Judy said.

"I got yours red, *naturally*."

They had given one another pocketbooks of colored imitation leather, handsomely outfitted with lipstick, powder and rouge compact, comb, and cigarette case.

"I *love* mine," Fuffy said.

"Me, too."

They swung the pocketbooks over their arms and started toward the Park. The streets were alive with children—little children in bright woollen snow suits, five- to ten-year-olds

70

whizzing by on skates and scooters. There were mere babies pushing toys with bells that rang as the wheels turned or riding in shiny red wagons. Smug little girls wheeled English coaches and fussed with dolls' blankets. Judy dangled her charm bracelet. "Look," she said.

They stopped while Fuffy admired the charms. "Oh, a little ice pick and a pair of tongs! And a lantern and a wheelbarrow! Honestly, it's absolutely the cutest one I've ever seen!"

"Daddy picked it out all by himself," Judy told her. There was pride in her voice, as though she were speaking of a backward child who had suddenly and amazingly refused to fit a square peg into a round hole.

They talked about what they had received. As they had made almost identical lists during recess at school, the conversation lacked variety.

"Goodness," Judy said, dodging a little girl on roller skates, "it's as much as your life's worth to walk on the street today!"

"Remember when you got the little automobile?" Fuffy asked. Her eyes were wistful. "I don't think I ever had as much fun any Christmas as the year you got that automobile. It was the year I got my Pogo stick."

"The way we tore around in it!" Judy smiled tolerantly. "I was late for dinner."

"How old were we when we got our tricycles?"

"Oh, we must have been *little*," Judy answered. "Five or six, I guess."

"I remember it perfectly."

They tacitly avoided walking in the Park and stayed on Fifth Avenue. The air was filled with the noises children make: screams, whistles, the sound of wheels on cement, the soft thud of balls, and laughter so shrill and mirthless that it could be heard over all the other sounds. Judy's hands grew cold in her new gloves and the seams of her stockings twisted on her legs.

71

They walked on and on, waiting sedately at corners for the lights to change, swinging their new bags from their arms. At Sixtieth Street they started back uptown. Judy's heels hurt where her shoes had rubbed against them and several times Fuffy stopped to adjust her stockings.

By the time they had reached the door to Fuffy's apartment on Seventy-ninth Street, they had grown silent. "Well, Merry Christmas *encore*, and thanks loads for the bag," Judy said.

Judy was surprised to see that it was not even noon when she reached home. The apartment was silent. Lois and her mother had gone out and her father lay on the living-room couch, asleep.

She took off her coat and hat and hung them in the hall closet and went into the living room. The little tree stood between the windows, heavy with ornaments. In the daylight it looked overburdened, as though its branches were not strong enough to carry the weight of so many things. She began rearranging her presents. There didn't seem to be so many now; the gloves were in her coat pocket, she was wearing the bracelet and one of the pairs of stockings, and she had taken the perfume to her room. She decided to put her things away and found that she could easily make them into one load. She put the stocking box Lois had given her in her bureau drawer and arranged the stockings in the compartments. Her new nightgown and silk pants she spread over the top of her old underwear.

Closing the drawer, she left the rest of her things lying on the bed and walked back to the living room. For a while she stood looking out of the window, jingling her bracelet against the glass. Then she walked over to the tree once more. Stooping down, she picked up the little crib with the twin babies. And then she sank to the floor. She could almost get under the lowest branches of the tree by ducking, and she edged closer to it.

72

Bits of silver rain touched her hair and the boughs overhead gave her a closed-in feeling, like being in a small house. She put the crib in her lap and unpinned the blankets, smoothed them out, and pinned them more tightly under the babies' chins. "Go to sleep," she said softly, and rocked the cradle lightly with her finger.

DAVE GERARD   *Courtesy of* Collier's

"I fixed it! I fixed it! You should've
tried this one first!"

By Clement C. Moore

A VISIT FROM ST. NICHOLAS

'Twas the night before Christmas, when all through the house
Not a creature was stirring, not even a mouse;
The stockings were hung by the chimney with care,
In hopes that St. Nicholas soon would be there.
The children were nestled all snug in their beds,
While visions of sugar-plums danced in their heads;
And mamma in her 'kerchief, and I in my cap,
Had just settled our brains for a long winter's nap,
When out on the lawn there rose such a clatter,
I sprang from the bed to see what was the matter.
Away to the window I flew like a flash,
Tore open the shutters and threw up the sash.
The moon on the breast of the new-fallen snow,
Gave the luster of mid-day to objects below,
When, what to my wondering eyes should appear,
But a miniature sleigh, and eight tiny reindeer,
With a little old driver, so lively and quick,
I knew in a moment it must be St. Nick.
More rapid than eagles his coursers they came,
And he whistled, and shouted, and called them by name;
"Now, *Dasher!* now, *Dancer!* now, *Prancer* and *Vixen!*

On, *Comet!* on *Cupid!* on, *Donner* and *Blitzen!*
To the top of the porch! to the top of the wall!
Now dash away! dash away! dash away all!"
As dry leaves that before the wild hurricane fly,
When they meet with an obstacle, mount to the sky,
So up to the house-top the coursers they flew,
With the sleigh full of toys, and St. Nicholas too.
And then, in a twinkling, I heard on the roof
The prancing and pawing of each little hoof.
As I drew in my head, and was turning around,
Down the chimney St. Nicholas came with a bound.
He was dressed all in fur, from his head to his foot,
And his clothes were all tarnished with ashes and soot;
A bundle of toys he had flung on his back,
And he looked like a peddler just opening his pack.
His eyes—how they twinkled! his dimples how merry!
His cheeks were like roses, his nose like a cherry!
His droll little mouth was drawn up like a bow,
And the beard of his chin was as white as the snow.
The stump of a pipe he held tight in his teeth,
And the smoke it encircled his head like a wreath;
He had a broad face and a round little belly
That shook, when he laughed, like a bowl full of jelly.
He was chubby and plump, a right jolly old elf,
And I laughed when I saw him, in spite of myself;
A wink of his eye and a twist of his head,
Soon gave me to know I had nothing to dread;
He spoke not a word, but went straight to his work,
And filled all the stockings; then turned with a jerk,
And laying his finger aside of his nose,
And giving a nod, up the chimney he rose;
He sprang to his sleigh, to his team gave a whistle,
And away they all flew like the down on a thistle.
But I heard him exclaim, ere he drove out of sight,

"Happy Christmas to all,

and to all

a good night!"

The new neighbor had a dreadful secret that made him kick dogs, scold children and fight with friends—on Christmas——

By J. Edgar Park

THE CHRISTMAS HERETIC

OUR STREET, like your street, might have been considered humdrum and ordinary. The usual folks lived in the usual houses. We got up about the same time and went to work about the same time and went to bed about half past ten—or our neighbors knew the reason why.

But there is a fantastic world just a millionth of an inch below the surface of the regular world. The only thing you really know about life is—that you never can tell. A new personality may drop into the most ordinary street and disturb the even surface with strange impossibilities. That is what happened on our street.

We were all away the day the Joneses moved in. Have you ever heard of anyone's moving on Thanksgiving Day? We never had. When we got home from Grandfather's the next morning we were astonished to see burlap and excelsior around the doors of No. 17. The draperies were up in the parlor. They must have got settled very quickly.

As I passed on my way to work, the remover's man, who evidently had stayed after the vans had left and who looked as if he had been working all night, was gathering up the remains of a broken chair or two that lay at the gate. He was very angry

79

and tired, and was communicating some of his wrath to our genial street cleaner, Tony, who was always on hand to make friends with everybody.

"I'll never move for him again!" he was saying as I passed. "Of all the bad-tempered cusses I ever met, he is the absolute limit, scolding and fussing all day. I never did hear such language, over a few broken chairs and crockery and such like!"

Just then a man, whom I afterward discovered to be Mr. Jones, came down the steps radiant with smiles and good humor, and placing a bill in the hands of the astonished man said, "That's for yourself! And a thousand thanks for all your care and work!" It was a strange sight, the disgruntled man just halted in his imprecations, gazing at a bill whose proportions evidently astounded him, and Mr. Jones with hearty hand outstretched to say good-by. Then the corner of the house hid them from my view, an incredible tableau.

Few people could win their way into the esteem of their neighbors as quickly as did Mr. Jones. He was the friend of every child on the street before he had been with us a week. His predecessor had been so bothered by children's riding their bicycles over his walks—for there was a lovely turn around the house—that he had put up a bit of barbed wire and a notice: "Children Keep Off. Police Take Notice." Mr. Jones took down the wire and taught one of our little girls how to ride round, coasting the last part of the way. He used the notice to fill up a cross drain so that the children could ride more smoothly. Our new neighbor proved to be an artist in the planning of the most satisfactory surprises. He always had an extra ticket for a ball game, an extra seat or two in his car when going for a ride.

Yet Mr. Jones was not to be explained simply as a kind-hearted man. There were complications. The remarks of the furniture remover lingered in my mind as an inexplicable mystery. And on Christmas Day I was reminded of that curious scene at his gate.

This newcomer had become such a favorite with us all that we vied with one another as to who should have the pleasure of entertaining him on Christmas Day. We found that he had had six invitations from our street alone. I will not conceal the fact that in three of these houses there were marriageable daughters—for Mr. Jones was a bachelor; but I think he would have been invited anyway. Each of us felt sure our new neighbor would come to us, for to each of us he had become so special and personal a friend that it had not struck us that he could seem so much a part of any other family as he did of ours. All the invitations he refused. We were surprised, and I confess the idea occurred to me that perhaps he was preparing some special surprise for the children on that day.

The children in our house were all up on Christmas morning at crack of dawn and rushed down at once to investigate the contents of their stockings. Mildred was overjoyed with her presents; but after going all over them twice she returned to her stocking again. Something troubled the child, I could see. Finding it really empty, she turned to her brother George and asked, "Did you get a present from Mr. Jones, George?" "No, that's funny, I didn't," he said. Somehow, Mr. Jones seemed to our children such a familiar friend that they had expected to be remembered by him. They had had great fun in preparing the little gifts they had dropped into his letter box, the evening before.

After the stocking presents had been admired and exhibited, it was still a long time till breakfast, and Mildred suggested they go out for a spin on their wheels, for it was sunny, snowless and mild. In ten minutes Mildred was back again, with indignant tears on her cheeks, and George scared and sobbing. They could hardly tell their story for emotion. They had been having a lovely time cycling about that beautiful turn around Mr. Jones's house. Mildred confessed that she had been going so fast that her wheel had gone off the asphalt walk onto the lawn; but she had often had the same experience before when Mr. Jones was teaching her.

This time, however, the window had opened and Mr. Jones had put his head out and had scolded them both terribly. How in the world, he said, could he keep a lawn looking like anything with all the kids in the street riding their wheels all over the grass. Give people an inch and they'll take an ell! If people cannot train their children to behave properly he wished they'd keep them at home! These were some of the remarks Mildred and George remembered and told us amid their sobs. I was incredulous till I looked out the window and saw Mr. Jones in his dressing gown, struggling with a tangle of barbed wire. He had put the notice back just where the Browns had had it, and was now fixing up the wire again.

The only explanation that we could find for Mr. Jones's behavior that evening at our Neighborhood Club Christmas Dance was that he must have been under the influence of liquor. Miss Farquerson left early, in tears. When I was going away after a heated political discussion into which he had drawn me unawares, and in which he had told me just what he thought of our popular local representative, I heard his voice, loud and rasping, informing Mrs. Francis Nosegood, "You folks in this neighborhood live in a puddle and think it is the world!"

It seemed, that evening, as we all retired for the night, that in no home in the street could Mr. Jones ever be forgiven. And yet, as I have indicated, his charm and goodness of heart, which asserted themselves again next morning, were so genuine that, in my mind at least, the experience of Christmas Day, like the remarks of the furniture remover, sank into the background of my consciousness as an inexplicable mystery. Next morning he took the wire and the notice down again and he re-won the affection of Mildred and George by a series of remarkably adroit and flattering attentions and kindnesses.

Mrs. Francis Nosegood, however, did not seem able to forgive him. She was the lady who lived in the big house at the corner. She had decided opinions. We were all familiar with her simple philosophy of life. People were either good or bad. Most people were at heart bad. They pretended to be good and often were able to deceive others for a time. But, sooner or later, to a shrewd observer like Mrs. Nosegood, they gave themselves away. Mr. Jones had given himself away. It remained for Mrs. Nosegood to follow up the clue and prove that his remark about the mud puddle was no mere accidental observation but a clear symptom of deep-seated moral depravity. It became her duty to expose his hypocrisy.

She despised us all for allowing Mr. Jones to "bribe" us into liking him again by what she called his "puny charities." Having nothing to do, she was immediately hot upon the scent of his past. We saw her coming out of the real-estate office with a triumphant air; she had a confidential interview with the mail carrier; she happened to pass just as Mr. Jones's housekeeper was going out shopping, and walked down town with her. Soon she began to wear an air of secret and invincible power whenever she haughtily acknowledged his greeting.

Meanwhile, Mr. Jones, seemingly in quiet unconsciousness of his new enemy, continued to act the part of Providence in our street, kind to just and unjust, naughty and good alike, with a sort of omnipotent casualness. He visited and entertained us all till he was to each of us a personal friend.

In a month or so Mrs. Nosegood left for a short visit in Manchester, New Hampshire. It seems the real-estate man had told her he understood Mr. Jones had moved here from that city. Mr. Jones, however, heard of her destination without any apparent uneasiness. She was gone for the better part of a week and returned triumphant. The next evening she called on us immediately after dinner. Her suspicions had been confirmed. On the twenty-ninth of February she had made her great discovery—that Mr. Jones had lived in the outskirts of Manchester with an old aunt who had brought him up since childhood. His violent bursts of temper had become notorious among the neighbors, and it was generally understood that relations between him and his wealthy old aunt were very unhappy at times, owing to these sudden fits of ungovernable rage. One day, the old aunt, who had been shopping all the afternoon, returned home in the best of health. According to his story, she was on her way upstairs when he heard her fall. Rushing up from the cellar where he was, he said, sorting apples, he found her lying in the hallway—dead. There was great indignation among the neighbors when this story became known; an inquiry was instituted and much testimony was heard; he was committed for trial, but in the end the jury disagreed and he was acquitted. Popular indignation, however, ran so high that he had to leave Manchester and, till Mrs. Nosegood's arrival, his whereabouts had been unknown. Mrs. Nosegood had talked on that day with many of the neighbors and had found that in Manchester Mr. Jones had evinced no special interest in children or neighbors. It was evident, she pointed out, that these traits were simply assumed here, as she had suspected all along, as a mere hypocritical screen.

The subject of her investigations happened to drop in before she left, and she took occasion to say to him in the most pointed manner, "I met some of your old acquaintances, Mr. Jones, in Manchester, these last few days."

"Well, well," he said, beaming on her in the most unconscious way in the world. "I didn't know I had any friends up there. Who were they, may I ask?"

"I met the Thompsons and the Blythes," she answered. As

she afterward told us, these were the two nearest neighbors to the house where Mr. Jones had lived.

She spoke with such a meaning stare that he seemed disconcerted and passed it off with, "Well, I hope they gave a good account of me, anyway!" Then he gaily changed the subject, and in a few moments Mrs. Nosegood, almost speechless with indignation, went away.

With incredible ingenuity Mrs. Nosegood now began to dig the pit beneath the unsuspecting feet of Mr. Jones. When Mr. Jones was absent her arguments were so cogent that we were almost convinced; but I confess all of them faded into thin air in the genial and kindly presence of that gentleman himself. All summer long Mrs. Nosegood sat in the window behind the curtain and watched the Jones house whenever Mr. Jones was at home. She went away for a well-earned vacation only after she had seen him off for his.

In the fall, a chemical laboratory in one of the upper rooms of the Jones house was added to the wireless equipment—as a further attraction to the boys of the neighborhood. Mr. Jones was a scientific expert of some kind in a large manufacturing concern and, according to the boys, was experimenting till late into the night with certain rare and deadly chemicals. This gave Mrs. Nosegood her next clue. It was now clear that the rich old aunt had been poisoned.

Thanksgiving Day came, the first anniversary of Mr. Jones's arrival. As usual, we went away the evening before to Grandfather's farm. When we returned the morning after Thanksgiving Day we heard of strange doings in our absence. It seemed that Mr. Jones had chosen that day in which to do his "spring cleaning." He had got two Polish girls to assist his housekeeper, and through the open windows could be heard the storming, growling voice of Mr. Jones, scolding and complaining at the poor women as they worked. This went on, the neighbors said, all day, till at six o'clock he let the girls go.

At the Thanksgiving reception at the Neighborhood Club, on the evening of Thanksgiving Day, he had insisted on relating to the whole company his troubles—the clumsy women, the way they had disarranged his books and instruments with bottomless stupidity. He vented his spleen on the whole company, complaining on the general incapacity of every one.

At this, Miss Farquerson, the pretty one from the house opposite, being a college girl and knowing her own mind, could stand it no longer, and told him just what she thought of him. The girl's genuine wrath became her very well. He stopped and looked at her fixedly for a moment, and then said, "Bah! The more I see of people the more thankful I am that my special investigation at this time is the various uses of arsenic!"

At this word, they told us, Mrs. Nosegood looked around triumphantly. Within a week she was back in Manchester, New Hampshire. She told the Thompsons and the Blythes of her further evidence. They put their heads together, and with the consent of the new tenant of the Jones house they made a thorough investigation of the house from cellar to attic. There were no results; but the apple closet in the cellar was locked and the key in the pocket of the owner, who happened to be away from home. The Blythes promised to investigate that closet as soon as he returned. Mrs. Nosegood came back to her armchair at the window, from which she kept track of every moment of Mr. Jones. He was friendly with every household on the street except her own and Miss Farquerson's, whom he apparently had never forgiven for her frank speech on Thanksgiving Day. Mrs. Nosegood rejoiced in this and missed no opportunity to bestow favors on that young lady, especially in the presence of Mr. Jones.

Christmas Day came again. Christmas trees or Christmas turkeys came to every door on the street except that of Mr. Jones. Early in the morning of Christmas Day he apparently came down and closed his dog outside his door and let him howl horribly there the rest of the hours of darkness, keeping all his neighbors awake. He made his housekeeper wash after breakfast and hung the entire wash out with his own hands, not, as usually, in the screened place behind the house, but on a rope tied between two trees on the front lawn. He then brought out his ash barrels, which the city teams were to call for next day, and put them in a row—he must have been saving them for the purpose for weeks—on the sidewalk in front of his house. Thus he effectively spoiled the looks of the street and gave a black eye to the whole neighborhood. All day long, he played at deafening volume the cheapest and most exasperating records he could find. At dinner hour he came out of the house, kicked the dog into howling again, and, making deep-track short cuts over all our lawns and flower beds, disappeared for a walk—thus giving Mrs. Nosegood a chance to go down from her watchtower for her dinner.

The usual Christmas Festival was held at our little Neighborhood Club that evening. We were all with Mrs. Nosegood now, heartily angry with Mr. Jones; we avoided him when he arrived. Mrs. Nosegood came in late and, beckoning to me, told me in tremendous excitement that she had just had a telegram from Manchester, New Hampshire, absolutely establishing Mr. Jones's guilt. He had poisoned his wealthy aunt with arsenic. She had a telegram from the Blythes saying that they had just discovered, under a barrel of rotten apples in the cellar closet, four papers full of a white powder and labeled "Arsenic."

Around the supper table we usually had speeches and toasts of a friendly and amusing nature. The laughter after one of these had died down when I discovered, to my astonishment, Mr. Jones upon his feet. He was about to make a speech. Mrs. Nosegood clutched at her telegram and looked at him with triumphant disdain.

"Friends," he began, "this is a great day in my life, and I am going to ask you to permit me to tell you a little about myself, if it will not bore you." There being no particular dissent, if no great enthusiasm, Mr. Jones continued: "It may surprise you to know that I lived, before arriving here, in Manchester, New Hampshire."

At this, Mrs. Nosegood, unable to contain herself any longer, leapt to her feet and with blazing eye cried out: "Mr. Jones, it may surprise you to know that we know a great deal more about you than you think. I have here in my hand a telegram establishing your guilt. Mr. Jones, your aunt did not die as a result of falling downstairs. She died as a result of arsenic poisoning and you were the murderer." With this she handed the telegram to Mr. Jones.

He read it twice and laid it down, with calmness, at his plate. "I have been guilty, very guilty in this matter, I confess," he said, "but to-night I am going to make a full confession to you all."

The old spell of his friendly courtesy seemed to be weaving itself around us once more. Mrs. Nosegood appealed to Miss Farquerson that he be not heard. But Miss Farquerson quietly answered, "I think it only fair to hear his side of the case, if he has one."

Mr. Jones, with simplicity, continued: "It evidently does not surprise you to know that before I came here I lived in Manchester, New Hampshire. The people among whom I lived were ordinary people; that is to say, they acted as if it were natural to be selfish, and as if there must be a special reason or a special occasion for any act of public spirit or good will. So, while living all the year as selfish lookers-after-themselves, they were terrible sentimentalists about Christmas and Thanksgiving. On these days they dabbled in a little amateurish way at those concerns which ought to have been the main business of their lives—true friendliness and neighborliness.

"After a while I found two homes in Manchester where there were friends who agreed with my point of view, and in process of time we came to live in three houses next one another—the Thompsons, the Blythes, and I. We formed a club founded upon our principles, and I should like to read you the constitution of that club." He took up a small piece of paper and read:

"Principles of the Three Hundred and Sixty-three Club

"1. Every one ought to be generous and thankful every day in the year.

"2. Nobody can be generous and thankful every day in the year.

"3. Therefore, be it enacted, that we, the members of this club, do observe as solemn festivals two days in every year, (a) The National Day of Grumbling and Growling, and (b) Devilmas Day. Into the first of these we shall try to concentrate all the necessary grumbling and growling which has to be indulged in by any decent man who is human. On it we shall try to locate those tasks (like moving or house cleaning) which cannot be accomplished by any one not a hypocrite, without tension, strain, and profanity. And on Devilmas Day we shall try to work off all the year's accumulated meanness which, even in the best of lives, must accumulate, and even by the best of men must somehow be worked off, if insanity is to be dodged. The rest of the three hundred and sixty-three days of the year we shall observe as Thanksgiving and Christmas Days.

"We lived for some years to our own great satisfaction and, I fear, to the utter mystification of our neighbors, in obedience to these principles. Then business changes made it necessary for me to move away.

89

"Last year I observed Devilmas Day, as you may remember, on the 25th of December by working off some of my accumulated irritation at the rudeness and carelessness of some of your children. This, together with my extremely irritated remark to Mrs. Nosegood, made me sure that a woman of her type would try to prove, from my past, her theory about me.

"My last action last Devilmas Day was to write to my friends, the Thompsons and Blythes, in Manchester, to tell them that an old woman named Nosegood would be there soon to look up my record. I told them to tell her I was suspected of killing my aunt. My aunt really never existed. I should not be so queer, perhaps, if I were not an only child of two only children.

"This telegram which I hold shows me that my friends in Manchester, true to their vows, are celebrating Devilmas Day in their own jovial fashion. My friends, I call you to witness that my celebration of these festivals has been just a concentration at my house of things that do happen elsewhere in our street all through the year."

We hung our heads, as one of us was guilty of premature ash barrels, one of an occasional public wash, and another of the nocturnal howling dog.

"My friends," he continued, "I was wrong. I am here to confess it heartily and to ask your pardon. Once a man ceases being a mere observer and becomes really entangled in life, he needs far more of an outlet for growling and devilment than I had supposed. I hereby renounce my previous plan and return with the rest of you to the method of trying to be as nice as possible two days in the year."

Turning to Mrs. Nosegood he continued: "It may astonish you to learn that right here under your eyes and without your knowledge has taken place one of the most thrilling of modern dramas. A would-be onlooker in your street has been entangled in life by love; or, to put the matter in a more conventional

90

way, Miss Farquerson and I have the honor to announce—"

When, after a few moments, Doctor Brown returned to the table and said that Mrs. Nosegood had recovered so far that he thought it was all right to send her home in the station hack, Mr. Jones came round and took the place she had so suddenly vacated beside Miss Farquerson.

"Well, well . . . 'Merry Christmas to the curviest
secretary in the entire Eastern Branch office'!"

"I happen to know he's loaded with tranquilizers."

Her mother asked for only one of the two most wonderful gifts in the world—and in trying to give the first, the little girl gave the second also.

By Elizabeth Morrow

A PINT OF JUDGMENT

THE Tucker family made out lists of what they wanted for Christmas. They did not trust to Santa Claus' taste or the wisdom of aunts and uncles in such an important matter. By the first week in December everybody had written out what he or she hoped to receive.

Sally, who was seven, when she could only print had sent little slips of paper up the chimney with her desires plainly set forth. She had wondered sometimes if neatly written requests like Ellen's were not more effective than the printed ones. Ellen was eight. She had asked last year for a muff and Santa had sent it.

Mother always explained that one should not expect to get all the things on the list: "Only what you want most, dear, and sometimes you have to wait till you are older for those."

For several years Sally had asked for a lamb and she had almost given up hope of finding one tied to her stocking on Christmas morning. She had also asked for a white cat and a dove and they had not come either. Instead a bowl of goldfish had been received. Now she wrote so plainly that there was no excuse for misunderstandings like this.

Derek still printed his list—he was only six and yet he had

received an Indian suit the very first time he asked for it. It was puzzling.

Caroline, called "Lovey" for short, just stood on the hearth rug and shouted "Dolly! Bow wow!" but anybody with Santa Claus' experience would know that rag dolls and woolly dogs were the proper presents for a four-year-old.

The lists were useful too in helping one to decide what to make for Father and Mother and the others for Christmas. The little Tuckers had been brought up by their grandmother in the belief that a present you made yourself was far superior to one bought in a store. Mother always asked for a great many things the children could make. She was always wanting knitted washcloths, pincushion covers, blotters and penwipers. Father needed pipe cleaners, calendars and decorated match boxes.

This year Sally longed to do something quite different for her mother. She was very envious of Ellen, who had started a small towel as her present, and was pulling threads for a fringed end.

"Oh! Ellen! How lovely that is!" she sighed. "It is a real grown-up present, just as if Aunt Elsie had made it."

"And it isn't half done yet," Ellen answered proudly. "Grandma is helping me with cross-stitch letters in blue and red for one end."

"If I could only make something nice like that! Can't you think of something for me?"

"A hemmed handkerchief?" suggested Ellen.

"Oh, no! Mother has lots of handkerchiefs."

"Yes, but when I gave her one for her birthday she said she had never had enough handkerchiefs. They were like asparagus."

"They don't look like asparagus," Sally replied, loath to criticize her mother but evidently confused. "Anyway, I don't want to give her a handkerchief."

"A penwiper?"

96

"No, I'm giving Father that."

"A new pincushion cover?"

"Oh! no, Ellen. I'm sick of those presents. I want it to be a big—lovely—Something—a great surprise."

Ellen thought a minute. She was usually resourceful and she did not like to fail her little sister. They had both been earning money all through November and perhaps this was a time to *buy* a present for Mother—even if Grandma disapproved.

"I know that Mother has made out a new list," she said. "She and Father were laughing about it last night in the library. Let's go and see if it is there."

They found two papers on the desk, unmistakably lists. They were typewritten. Father's was very short: "Anything wrapped up in tissue paper with a red ribbon around it."

"Isn't Father funny?" giggled Ellen. "I'd like to fool him and do up a dead mouse for his stocking."

Mother had filled a full page with her wants. Ellen read out slowly:

> Pair of Old English silver peppers
> Fur coat
> ("Father will give her that.")
> Umbrella
> Robert Frost's Poems
> Silk stockings
> Muffin tins
> Small watering pot for house plants
> Handkerchiefs
> Guest towels
> ("Aren't you glad she asked for that?" Sally broke in.)
> Knitted washcloths
> A red pencil
> A blue pencil
> Ink eraser
> Pen holders

Rubber bands
Hot water bag cover
A quart of judgment

This last item was scribbled in pencil at the bottom of the sheet.

As Ellen finished reading, she said with what Sally called her "little-mother air," "You needn't worry at all about Mother's present. There are lots of things here you could make for her. Couldn't you do a hot water bag cover if Grandma cut it out for you? I'm sure you could. You take a nice soft piece of old flannel . . ."

"No! No! Nothing made out of old flannel!" cried Sally. "That's such a baby thing. I want it to be different—and a great surprise. I wish I could give her the silver peppers. . . . That's the first thing on her list; but I've only got two dollars and three cents in my bank and I'm afraid that's not enough."

"Oh! It isn't the peppers she wants most!" cried Ellen. "It's the *last* thing she wrote down—that 'quart of judgment.' I know for I heard her tell Father, 'I need that more than anything else . . . even a pint would help.' And then they both laughed."

"What is judgment?" asked Sally.

"It's what the judge gives—a judgment," her sister answered. "It must be something to do with the law."

"Then I know it would cost more than two dollars and three cents," said Sally. "Father said the other day that nothing was so expensive as the law."

"But she only asked for a pint," Ellen objected. "A pint of anything couldn't be very expensive, unless it was diamonds and rubies."

"She wanted a *quart*," Sally corrected. "And she just said that afterwards about a pint helping because she knew a whole quart would be too much for us to buy."

98

"A hot water bag cover would be lots easier," cautioned Ellen.

"I don't want it to be easy!" cried Sally. "I want it to be what she wants!"

"Well, perhaps you could get it cheap from Uncle John," Ellen suggested. "He's a lawyer—and he's coming to dinner tonight, so you could ask him."

Sally was not afraid to ask Uncle John anything. He never laughed at her or teased her as Uncle Tom sometimes did and he always talked to her as if she were grown up. On any vexed question he always sided with her and Ellen. He had even been known to say before Mother that coconut cake was good for children and that seven-thirty for big girls of seven and eight was a disgracefully early bedtime. He thought arctics unnecessary in winter and when a picnic was planned, he always knew it would be a fine day.

Sally drew him into the little library that evening and shut the door carefully.

"Is it something very important?" he asked as they seated themselves on the sofa.

"Yes," she answered. "Awfully important. It's a secret. You won't tell, will you?"

"No, cross my heart and swear. What is it?"

"It's—it's . . . Oh—Uncle John—what *is* judgment? I must get some."

"Judgment? That *is* an important question, my dear." Uncle John seemed puzzled for a moment. "And it is hard to answer. Why do you bother about that now? You have your whole life to get it. . . . Come to me again when you're eighteen."

"But I can't wait so long. I must get it right away. Mother wants it for a Christmas present. She put on her list, 'A quart of judgment.' She said even a pint would help."

Uncle John laughed. He threw back his head and shouted.

Sally had never seen him laugh so hard. He shook the sofa with his mirth and tears rolled down his cheeks. He didn't stop until he saw that Sally was hurt—and even then a whirlwind of chuckles seized him occasionally.

"I'm not laughing at you, Sally darling," he explained at last, patting her shoulder affectionately, "but at your mother. She doesn't need judgment. She has it. She always has had it. She's a mighty fine woman—your mother. She must have put that on her list as a joke."

"Oh no! Excuse me, Uncle John," Sally protested. "She told Father she wanted it more than anything else. Wouldn't it be a good Christmas present?"

"Perfectly swell," her uncle answered. "The most useful thing on earth. I've never heard of its being given for Christmas but it would be wonderful. If you have any left over, give me some."

"Why, I was going to ask you to sell me some," Sally explained. "Ellen said you would surely have it."

Just then Mother called, "Ellen! Sally! Bedtime. Hurry, dears. It's twenty minutes to eight already."

"Bother!" exclaimed Sally. "I'm always having to go to bed. But please tell me where I can get it. At Macy's? Delia is taking us to town tomorrow."

"No, my dear," he answered. "Macy sells almost everything but not that. It doesn't come by the yard."

"Girls!" Mother's voice again.

"Oh! Quick, Uncle John," whispered Sally. "Mother's coming. I'll have to go. Just tell me. What *is* judgment?"

"It is *sense*, Sally," he answered, quite solemn and serious now. "Common sense. But it takes a lot . . ." He could not finish the sentence for at this point Mother opened the door and carried Sally off to bed.

The little girl snuggled down under the sheets very happily. Uncle John had cleared her mind of all doubt. She had only

100

time for an ecstatic whisper to Ellen before Delia put out the light: "It's all right about Mother's present. Uncle John said it would be 'swell.'" Then she began to calculate: "If it is just *cents, common cents,* I have ever so many in my bank and I can earn some more. Perhaps I have enough already."

With this delicious hope she fell asleep.

The first thing after breakfast the next morning she opened her bank. It was in the shape of a fat man sitting in a chair. When you put a penny in his hand he nodded his head in gratitude as the money slipped into his safety-box. Sally unscrewed the bottom of this and two dollars and three cents rolled out. It was not all in pennies. There were several nickels, three dimes, two quarters and a fifty-cent piece. It made a rich-looking pile. Sally ran to the kitchen for a pint cup and then up to the nursery to pour her wealth into it. No one was there in the room to hear her cry of disappointment. The coins did not reach to the "Half" marked on the measure.

But there was still hope. The half dollar and quarters when they were changed would lift the level of course. She put all the silver into her pocket and consulted Ellen.

Her sister had passed the penny-bank stage and kept her money in a blue leather purse which was a proud possession. Aunt Elsie had given it to her last Christmas. It had two compartments and a small looking-glass—but there was very little money in it now. Ellen had already bought a good many presents. She was only able to change one quarter and one dime.

"Let's ask Derek," she said. "He loves to open his bank because he can use the screwdriver of his tool set."

Derek was delighted to show his savings—forty-five cents—but he was reluctant to give them all up for one quarter and two dimes. It would mean only three pieces to drop into the chimney of the little red house which was his bank.

"They don't clink at all," he complained, experimenting with the coins Sally held out. "You'll take all my money. I won't have hardly anything."

"You'll have *just* as much money to spend," explained Ellen.

"Yes," Derek admitted, "but not to jingle. I like the jingle. It sounds so much more."

He finally decided to change one nickel and one dime.

Then Grandma changed a dime and Sally had sixty pennies all together to put into the pint cup. They brought the pile up about an inch.

When Father came home that night she asked him to change the fifty-cent piece, the quarter and the three nickels, but he did not have ninety cents in pennies and he said that he could not get them until Monday and now it was only Saturday.

"You understand, Sally," he explained looking down into his little daughter's anxious face, "you don't have any more money after this is changed. It only *looks* more."

"I know, but I want it that way," she answered.

On Monday night he brought her the change and it made a full inch more of money in the cup. Still it was less than half a pint. Sally confided her discouragement to Ellen.

"Are you sure," asked her sister, "that it was this kind of present Mother wanted? She never asked for money before."

"I'm sure," Sally replied. "Uncle John said it was *cents* and that it would take a lot. Besides she prayed for it in church yesterday—so she must want it awfully."

"Prayed for it!" exclaimed Ellen in surprise.

"Yes, I heard her. It's that prayer we all say together. She asked God for 'two cents of all thy mercies.'"

"But if she wants a whole pint why did she only ask for 'two cents?'" demanded the practical Ellen.

"I don't know," Sally answered. "Perhaps she thought it would be greedy. Mother is never greedy."

For several days things were at a standstill. Ellen caught a cold and passed it on to Sally and Derek. They were all put to bed and could do very little Christmas work. While Mother read aloud to them Sally finished her penwiper for Father and decorated a blotter for Uncle John—but sewing on Grandma's pincushion cover was difficult because the pillow at Sally's back kept slipping and she couldn't keep the needle straight. There seemed no way of adding anything to the pint cup.

"Mother, how could I earn some money quickly before Christmas?" Sally asked the first day that she was up.

"You have already earned a good deal, dear," Mother said. "Do you really need more?"

"Yes, Mother, lots more."

"How about getting 100 in your number work? Father gives you a dime every time you do that."

"Yes," sighed Sally, "but it's very hard to get all the examples right. Don't you think when I get all right but one he might give me nine cents?"

"No," said Mother laughing. "Your father believes that nothing is good in arithmetic but 100."

She did earn one dime that way and then school closed, leaving no hope for anything more before Christmas.

On the twentieth of December there was a windfall. Aunt Elsie, who usually spent the holidays with them, was in the South and she sent Mother four dollars—one for each child for a Christmas present. "She told me to buy something for you," Mother explained, "but I thought perhaps you might like to spend the money yourselves—later on—during vacation."

"Oh! I'd like my dollar right away!" cried Sally delightedly. "And," she added rather shamefacedly, "Lovey is so little . . . do you think she needs all her money? Couldn't she give me half of hers?"

"Why, Sally, I'm surprised at you!" her mother answered. "I can't take your little sister's share for you. It wouldn't be fair. I am buying a new *Benjamin Bunny* for Lovey."

Aunt Elsie's gift brought the pennies in the pint cup a little above the half mark.

On the twenty-first Sally earned five cents by sweeping off the back porch. This had been a regular source of revenue in the fall, but when the dead leaves gave place to snow Mother forbade the sweeping. On the twenty-first there was no snow and Sally was allowed to go out with her little broom.

On the twenty-second Ellen and Sally went to a birthday party and Sally found a shiny bright dime in her piece of birthday cake. This helped a little. She and Ellen spent all their spare moments in shaking up the pennies in the pint measure—but they could not bring the level much above "One Half." Ellen was as excited over the plan now as Sally and she generously added her last four cents to the pile.

On the twenty-third Sally made a final desperate effort. "Mother," she said, "Uncle John is coming to dinner again tonight. Do you think he would be willing to give me my birthday dollar now?"

Mother smiled as she answered slowly—"But your birthday isn't till June. Isn't it rather strange to ask for your present so long ahead? Where is all this money going to?"

"It's a secret! My special secret!" cried the little girl, taking her mother's reply for consent.

Uncle John gave her the dollar. She hugged and kissed him with delight and he said, "Let me always be your banker, Sally. I'm sorry you are so hard up, but don't take any wooden nickels."

" 'Wooden nickels,' " she repeated slowly. "What are they? Perhaps they would fill up the bottom—"

"Of your purse?" Uncle John finished the sentence for her. "No, no, my dear. They are a very poor bottom for anything—and they are worse on top."

"It wasn't my purse," said Sally. "It was—but it's a secret."

When Father changed the birthday dollar into pennies he said, "You are getting to be a regular little miser, my dear. I don't understand it. Where is all this money going to?"

"That's just what Mother asked," Sally answered. "It's a secret. You'll know on Christmas. Oh, Father, I think I have enough now!"

But she hadn't. The pennies seemed to melt away as they fell into the measure. She and Ellen took them all out three times and put them back again, shaking them sideways and forwards, but it was no use. They looked a mountain on the nursery floor but they shrank in size the moment they were put inside that big cup. The mark stood obstinately below "Three Quarters."

"Oh! Ellen!" sobbed Sally after the third attempt. "Not even a pint! It's a horrid mean little present! All my presents are horrid. I never can give nice things like you. Oh dear, what shall I do!"

"Don't cry, Sally—please don't," said Ellen, trying to comfort her little sister. "It's not a horrid present. It will look lovely when you put tissue paper around it and lots of red ribbons and a card. It *sounds* so much more than it looks," Ellen went on, giving the cup a vigorous jerk. "Why don't you print on your card 'Shake well before opening,' like our cough mixture?"

"I might," assented Sally, only partly reassured.

She had believed up to the last moment that she would be able to carry out her plan. It was vaguely associated in her mind with a miracle. Anything might happen at Christmas time but this year she had hoped for too much. It was so late now however that there was nothing to do but make the outside of her gift look as attractive as possible. She and Ellen spent most of the afternoon before Christmas wrapping up their presents. The pint cup was a little awkward in shape but they had it well covered and the red satin ribbon gathered tight at the top before Grandma made the final bow. It was a real rosette, for Sally had asked for something special.

Christmas Eve was almost more fun than Christmas. The Tuckers made a ceremony of hanging up their stockings. The whole family formed a line in the upper hall with Father at the head, the youngest child on his back, and then they marched downstairs keeping step to a Christmas chant. It was a home-made nonsense verse with a chorus of "Doodley-doodley, doodley-doo!" which everybody shouted. By the time they reached the living-room the line was in wild spirits.

The stockings were always hung in the same places. Father had the big armchair to the right of the fireplace and Mother the large mahogany chair opposite it, Lovey had a small white chair borrowed from the nursery. Derek tied his sock to the hook which usually held the fire tongs above the wood basket (it was a very inconvenient place but he liked it) and Ellen and Sally divided the sofa.

After the stockings were put up, one of the children recited the Bible verses, "And there were in the same country shepherds abiding in the field, keeping watch over their flock by night," through "And Mary kept all these things and pondered them in her heart." Sally had said the verses last Christmas— Ellen the year before—and now it was Derek's turn. He only forgot once and Ellen prompted him softly.

Then they all sang "Holy Night"—and Father read " 'Twas the Night Before Christmas." Last of all, the children distributed their gifts for the family—with a great many stern directions: "Mother, you won't look at this till tomorrow, will you? Father, you promise not to peek?" Then they went up to bed and by morning Father and Mother and Santa Claus had the stockings stuffed full of things.

It went off as usual this year but through all the singing and the shouting Sally had twinges of disappointment thinking of

Mother's unfinished present. She had squeezed it into Mother's stocking with some difficulty. Then came Ellen's lovely towel and on top of that Derek's calendar which he had made in school.

There was a family rule at the Tuckers' that stockings were not opened until after breakfast. Mother said that presents on an empty stomach were bad for temper and digestion and though it was hard to swallow your cereal Christmas morning, the children knew it was no use protesting.

The first sight of the living-room was wonderful. The place had completely changed over night. Of course the stockings were knobby with unknown delights, and there were packages everywhere, on the tables and chairs, and on the floor big express boxes that had come from distant places, marked "Do Not Open Until Christmas."

Some presents are of such unmistakable shape that they cannot be hidden. Last year Derek had jumped right onto his rocking horse shouting, "It's mine! I know it's mine!" This morning he caught sight of a drum and looked no further. Lovey fell upon a white plush bunny. A lovely pink parasol was sticking out of the top of Sally's stocking and Ellen had a blue one. They just unfurled them over their heads and then watched Father and Mother unwrapping their presents.

The girls felt Derek and Lovey were very young because they emptied their stockings without a look towards the two big armchairs. That was the most thrilling moment, when your own offering came to view and Mother said, "Just what I wanted!" or Father, "How did you know I needed a penwiper?"

Mother always opened the children's presents first. She was untying the red ribbon on Ellen's towel now and reading the card which said "Every stitch a stitch of love." As she pulled off the tissue paper, she exclaimed, "What beautiful work! And what exquisite little stitches! Ellen—I am proud of you. This is a charming guest towel. Thank you, dear, so much."

"Grandma marked the cross-stitch for me," explained Ellen, "but I did all the rest myself."

Sally shivered with excitement as Mother's hand went down into her stocking again and tugged at the tin cup.

"Here is something very heavy," she said. "I can't guess what it is, and the cards say '*Merry Christmas to Mother from Sally. Shake well before opening.*' Is it medicine or cologne?"

Nobody remembered just what happened after that. Perhaps Grandma's bow was not tied tightly enough, perhaps Mother tilted the cup as she shook it, but in a moment all the pennies were on the floor. They rolled everywhere, past the chairs, into the grate, under the sofa and on to the remotest corners of the room. There was a terrific scramble. Father and Mother and Ellen and Sally and Derek, even Grandma and Lovey got down on their hands and knees to pick them up. They bumped elbows and knocked heads together and this onrush sent the coins flying everywhere. The harder they were chased the more perversely they hid themselves. Out of the hubbub Mother cried, "Sally dear, what is this? I don't understand. All your Christmas money for me? Darling, I can't take it."

Sally flung herself into her mother's arms with a sob. "Oh! you must!" she begged. "I'm sorry it's not a whole pint. I tried so hard. You said—you *said*—you wanted it most of all."

" 'Most of all?' "

"Yes, judgment, *cents*. Uncle John said it was cents. You said even a pint would help. Won't half a pint be some good?"

Father and Mother and Grandma all laughed then. Father laughed almost as hard as Uncle John did when he first heard of Mother's list, and he declared that he was going to take Sally into the bank as a partner. But Mother lifted the little girl into her lap and whispered. "It's the most wonderful present I ever had. There's nothing so wonderful as sense—except love."

"I'm afraid she isn't quite right for the part."

AN ALPHABET OF CHRISTMAS

A   is for Animals who shared the stable.

B   for the Babe with their manger for cradle.

C   for the Carols so blithe and so gay.

D   for December, the twenty-fifth day.

E   for the Eve when we're all so excited.

F   for the Fun when the tree's at last lighted.

G   is the Goose which you all know is fat.

H   is the Holly you stick in your hat.

I   for the Ivy that clings to the wall.

J   is for Jesus, the cause of it all.

K   for the Kindness begot by this feast.

L   is the Light shining way in the east.

M   for the Mistletoe, all green and white.

N   for the Nowells we sing Christmas night.

O   for the Oxen, the first to adore Him.

P   for the Presents Wise Men laid before Him.

Q   for the Queerness that this should have been
Near two thousand years before you were seen.

R   for the Reindeer leaping the roofs.

S   for the Stockings that Santa Claus stuffs.

T   for the Toys, the Tinsel, the Tree.

U is for Us—the whole family.
V is for Visitors bringing us cheer.
W is Welcome to the happy New Year.
X Y Z bother me! All I can say,
Is this is the end of my Christmas lay.
So now to you all, wherever you be,
A merry, merry Christmas, and many may you see!

By Guyan Lewis

A BACK-HANDED ALPHABET
OF CHRISTMAS

A   is for All-we-go-through for one day.

B   is the Bills we soon have to pay.

C   is for Cards from those we forget.

D   is for Deficit, Debit and Debt.

E   is for Evergreen sap in the rug.

F   for the Fights of the little ones-ug!

G   for Gift-wrapping that takes half the night.

H   for the Hash that makes next week a blight.

I   for Indigestion after nibbling all day.

J   for the Junk we can't throw away.

K   for the visiting Kith and their Kin.

L   for the Labor to keep harsh words in.

M   is for Monograms—just slightly wrong.

N   is for Noise that goes on too long.

O   for the Office's perilous party.

P   for the Punch—more heart-burning than hearty.

Q   for the Quarrels over who will dine where.

R   is Recovering—with medical care.

S   is for Sales—half price tomorrow!

T   is the Tips we give or we sorrow.

U   for Undecorating the house and the tree.

V   for the Voices carolling off key.

W   for Words (x!*x+!) that describe Christmas ties.

X   for Xchanging wrong colors and size.

Y   is for Yearning not to give but to get.

Z   is the end of my sad alphabet.
    I can dig up only one note of slight cheer.
    It can't happen again for another whole year.

JACK MARROW

"A child can put it together
if his father lets him alone."

SID GORDIN   *Courtesy of* Collier's

"He had a long white beard, a bright red suit,
and a sled driven by eight tiny reindeer."

No one believed he was serious when he wrote about his improbable, mind-dazing recipe for stuffed, roasted turkey.

But it works—though so must the daring, justly famous cooks who try it.

By Morton Thompson

HOW TO COOK A TURKEY

WHEN I was running the old column, I
used to run quite a few food columns in on my parishioners.
But it was only after two, three years that they got so they
took me seriously enough to try the recipes out.

There was one, for instance, on how to cook a turkey. The
first year that column ran, it was received with broad grins.
All my readers thought I was kidding. The second year a few
tried it, the rest kept on grinning. The third year there were
more converts. About the time of the fourth year, the Domestic
Science Editor of the paper asked me if I wouldn't give a lecture on How to Cook a Turkey before a group of women in the
paper's auditorium. Naturally, feeling the way I do about
women and food, I said yes. I was sorry later. When I got on
that damned rostrum and looked out at those bright, merry
faces all gathered to see a mere man make a jerk of himself
fooling around with stuff they felt belonged in a woman's prov-
ince, I got kind of sore. I decided to snow them under.

On the platform was a glistening stove, a table with every
known appliance. There was a cupboard full of a great many
spices. Not all the spices. Just the ones a woman could understand and accept. I started calling for things. Each new thing

117

I called for, the Domestic Science Editor would hand me, and everything she handed me brought out a howl of delight from the women. Finally I had the stuffing all made. They subsided from their mad, Bacchic laughter long enough to howl for the stuff to be passed around. Wanted to smell it and laugh some more, I guess. I handed the bowl to the Domestic Science gal and she gave it to a woman in the first row. They started to pass it around. I went to work on the turkey. Kind of a complicated deal, fixing the bird to receive the dressing. Halfway through I noticed the place was kind of still. I looked up and called for the bowl of stuffing. It came up to the platform in perfect silence. It was empty. They'd eaten it raw. They just didn't have anything to say, and they weren't laughing any more, and the next year a very decent percentage of those who read the "How to Cook a Turkey" column actually tried it.

The thing is, all this took five years.

And if *you* have to read it for five years, he said bitterly, before you get around to taking it seriously, I'll be very happy. Just so you try it.

How to Cook a Turkey

If you want a well-cooked dinner the labor of preparing must be equal to the pleasure of your enjoying. If the labor is greater, the solace is less. If the labor is trifling, so also will be your pleasure. The path from the kitchen to the dining room is a short road—not so long as happiness, nor so short as a dyspeptic's smile. In your preparations for that walk remember these things and rejoice that no merchant and no wizard can offer for sale or gift or loan your own labor, the priceless ingredient implicit in whatever food you serve.

I have found it unwise to buy a turkey from a roadside farm. Many honest farmers raise their own and raise them well; some racketeers buy up worthless birds for the holiday occasion, put

118

up a sign reading, "Honest Hiram's Turkey Ranch—Turkeys Cheap!" and move elsewhere on the day after Thanksgiving or Christmas. But even if you know your farmer, be sure to let your bird rest a day or so or three or four after it has been killed. Fresh-killed meat of almost any kind is the most undesirable, least digestible, toughest, least flavorsome of comestibles. There was a time when freshness was a warrant against impurity—when meat left standing collected germs and was unhealthy. People put up with the toughness and bad flavor as the least of two evils. This is a day of rigidly supervised packing and refrigeration. Disease dangers in kept meats are entirely over, providing you allow Common Sense to keep as strong a hand on your purse as Thrift.

The turkey should not be less than sixteen pounds and not more than twenty-two. If it is eighteen pounds or more, buy a hen. You will get more breast. I buy mine from a butcher— usually in some large market. I get a better price as a rule, and I know it has been properly kept. When he eliminates the head, see that he chops it off so as to leave as much neck as possible. Have him peel back the neck skin and remove the neck from under the skin, close as possible to the shoulders. The tube of neck skin thus left will be admirable for stuffing with whatever stuffing is left over. When he cleans the bird have him make a small opening and skewer it shut, using string between the pegs, like old-fashioned lace shoes or a peasant bodice.

Rub the bird inside and out with salt and pepper.

In a stewpan put the chopped gizzard and the neck and heart, to which add

> one bay leaf
> one teaspoon of paprika
> half a teaspoon of coriander
> one clove of garlic

four cups of water

salt to taste

Let this simmer while you go ahead with the dressing.

In one bowl put

one diced apple

one diced orange

a large can of crushed pineapple

grated rind of one half a lemon

one can of drained water chestnuts

three tablespoons of chopped, preserved ginger

In another bowl put

two teaspoons of Colman's mustard

two teaspoons of caraway seed

three teaspoons of celery seed

two teaspoons of poppy seed

two and a half teaspoons of oregano

one well-crushed large bay leaf

one teaspoon of black pepper

one half teaspoon of mace

four tablespoons of well-chopped parsley

four or five finely minced cloves of garlic

four cloves, minus the heads and well chopped

one half teaspoon of turmeric

four large, well-chopped onions

six well-chopped stalks of celery

one half teaspoon of marjoram

one half teaspoon of summer savory

one tablespoon of poultry seasoning

salt to taste

In another bowl dump

three packages of bread crumbs, bought at a bakery

three quarters of a pound of ground veal

one quarter of a pound of ground fresh pork

one quarter of a pound of butter

all the fat (first rendered) that you have been able to
find and pry loose from the turkey

Mix in each bowl the contents of each bowl. When each bowl is well mixed, mix the three of them together. And mix it well. Mix it with your hands. Mix it until your forearms and wrists ache. Then mix it some more. Now toss it enough so that it isn't any longer a doughy mass.

Stuff your turkey, but not too full. Pretty full, though. Stuff the neck and tie the end. Skewer the bird. Tie the strings.

Turn on your oven full force and let it get red hot.

Put your bird on the drip pan, or, best of all, breast down in a rack.

In a cup make a paste of
two egg yolks
one teaspoon of Colman's mustard
one clove of minced garlic
one tablespoon of onion juice
one half teaspoon of salt
two pinches of cayenne pepper
one teaspoon of lemon juice
enough sifted flour to make a stiff paste

Take a pastry brush or an ordinary big paintbrush and stand by. Put your bird into the red-hot oven. Let it brown all over. Remove the turkey. Turn your oven down to 325 degrees. Now, while the turkey is sizzling hot, paint it completely all over with the paste. Put it back in the oven. The paste will have set in a few minutes. Drag it out again. Paint every nook and cranny of it once more. Put it back in the oven. Keep doing this until you haven't any more paste left.

To the giblet-neck-liver-heart gravy that has been simmering add
one cup of cider

121

Don't let it cook any more. Stir it well. Keep it warm on top of the oven. This is your basting fluid. Baste the bird every fifteen minutes! That means you will baste it from twelve to fifteen times. After the bird has cooked about an hour and a half turn it on its stomach, back in the air, and let it cook in that position until the last fifteen minutes, when you restore it to its back again. That is, unless you use a rack. If you use a rack don't turn it on its back until the last half hour. It ought to cook at least four hours and a half to five hours and a half.

When you remove the turkey it will be dead black.

You will think, "My God! I have ruined it!" Be calm. Take a tweaser and pry loose the paste coating. It will come off readily. Beneath this burnt, harmless, now worthless shell the bird will be golden and dark brown, succulent, giddy-making with wild aromas, crisp and crunchable and crackling. The meat beneath this crazing panorama of lip-wetting skin will be wet, juice will spurt from it in tiny fountains high as the handle of the fork plunged into it; the meat will be white, crammed with mocking flavor, delirious with things that rush over your palate and are drowned and gone as fast as you can swallow; cut a little of it with a spoon, it will spread on bread as eagerly and readily as soft wurst.

You do not have to be a carver to eat this turkey; speak harshly to it and it will fall apart.

This is the end of it. All but the dressing. No pen, unless it were filled with Thompson's gravy, can describe Thompson's dressing, and there is not paper enough in the world to contain the thoughts and adjectives it would set down, and not marble enough to serve for its monuments.

TED KEY

"Did we send *them* one?"

Mother Goose Continued for Christmas

By Anna Marion Smith

"There was an old woman
Who lived in a shoe,
Who had so many children
She didn't know what to do
She gave them some broth
Without any bread
And whipped them all soundly
And sent them to bed."

Now it happened that Santa Claus,
　　Passing that way,
Peeped into the shoe top
　　And saw how they lay—
With their round, rosy faces
　　All shining with tears,
And resolved to do something
　　To comfort the dears.

So while they were sleeping
　　In woful array,
He bundled those children
　　Right into his sleigh;
And cracking his whip
　　As his reindeers sped forth,
Away they all flew
　　To his home in the North.

What wonders he showed them,
  Such beautiful toys!
Such dolls for the girls,
  And such drums for the boys!
Such farms and such stables,
  Such monkeys and bears,
Such dishes and tables
  And tiny dolls' chairs!

And when they had seen
  All the wonderful things
Which each winter, at Christmas,
  Dear Santa Claus brings,
He gave them, to make
  Their enchantment complete,
Just all of the candy
  And cake they could eat.

When they told of their travels,
  Their mother, it seems,
Only laughed, and declared
  They were nothing but dreams.
I am sure, though, things *must*
  Have occurred as they say,
Else why were they, all of them,
  Ill the next day?

Two kings came loaded with great riches, but the third brought the gift of tenderness to a child on the first Christmas.

By Heywood Broun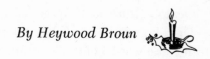

FRANKINCENSE AND MYRRH

ONCE there were three kings in the East and they were wise men. They read the heavens and they saw a certain strange star by which they knew that in a distant land the King of the World was to be born. The star beckoned to them and they made preparations for a long journey.

From their palaces they gathered rich gifts, gold and frankincense and myrrh. Great sacks of precious stuffs were loaded on the backs of the camels which were to bear them on their journey. Everything was in readiness, but one of the wise men seemed perplexed and would not come at once to join his two companions, who were eager and impatient to be on their way in the direction indicated by the star.

They were old, these two kings, and the other wise man was young. When they asked him he could not tell why he waited. He knew that his treasures had been ransacked for rich gifts for the King of Kings. It seemed that there was nothing more which he could give, and yet he was not content.

He made no answer to the old men who shouted to him that the time had come. The camels were impatient and swayed and snarled. The shadows across the desert grew longer. And still the young king sat and thought deeply.

At length he smiled, and he ordered his servants to open the great treasure sack upon the back of the first of his camels. Then he went into a high chamber to which he had not been since he was a child. He rummaged about and presently came out and approached the caravan. In his hand he carried something which glinted in the sun.

The kings thought that he carried some new gift more rare and precious than any which they had been able to find in all their treasure rooms. They bent down to see, and even the camel drivers peered from the backs of the great beasts to find out what it was which gleamed in the sun. They were curious about this last gift for which all of the caravan had waited.

And the young king took a toy from his hand and placed it upon the sand. It was a dog of tin, painted white, and speckled with black spots. Great patches of paint had worn away and left the metal clear, and that was why the toy shone in the sun as if it had been silver.

The youngest of the wise men turned a key in the side of the little black and white dog and then he stepped aside so that the kings and the camel drivers could see. The dog leaped high in the air and turned a somersault. He turned another and another and then fell over on his side and lay there with a set and painted grin upon his face.

A child, the son of a camel driver, laughed and clapped his hands, but the kings were stern. They rebuked the youngest of the wise men and he paid no attention but called to his chief servant to make the first of all of the camels kneel. Then he picked up the toy of tin and, opening the treasure sack, placed his last gift with his own hands in the mouth of the sack so that it rested safely upon the soft bags of incense.

"What folly has seized you?" cried the eldest of the wise men.

130

"Is this a gift to bear to the King of Kings in the far country?"

And the young man answered and said: "For the King of Kings there are gifts of great richness, gold and frankincense and myrrh.

"But this," he said, "is for the child in Bethlehem."

By Dorothy Parker

THE MAID-SERVANT AT THE INN

"It's queer," she said, "I see the light
    As plain as I beheld it then,
All silver-like and calm and bright—
    We've not had stars like that again!

"And she was such a gentle thing
    To birth a baby in the cold.
The barn was dark and frightening—
    This new one's better than the old.

"I mind my eyes were full of tears,
    For I was young, and quick distressed,
But she was less than me in years
    That held a son against her breast.

"I never saw a sweeter child—
    The little one, the darling one!—
I mind I told her, when he smiled
    You'd know he was his mother's son.

"It's queer that I should see them so—
  The time they came to Bethlehem
Was more than thirty years ago;
  I've prayed that all is well with them."

His mother did not want Him to go back.

"We had trouble getting reservations there before,"
she reminded Him.

By Bob Considine

WELL, A LITTLE MORE TIME . . .

HE HAD grown a bit older through the nearly 2,000 years. And He had been working too hard. The phones had been going night and day, for centuries, and there were millions of newcomers He hadn't been able to meet as yet.

His mother, of course, was the first to notice the few gray hairs around His temples. Quietly, but firmly, she suggested that He get away for a spell, and just before His birthday He decided it might be a pretty good suggestion, at that. He went to the window of His study one clear night and looked things over, trying to pick a vacation spot.

There were more than 30,000,000,000 worlds to tempt Him. All these, of the countless billions more, had passed through the trying years of war and want and had settled down to a point where peace had become an estate much more exciting to their peoples than war. He mulled over which of them He would visit, for He had not been to any of them for a time. But then a distant memory stirred itself and, searching the enormous oval of the littered sky, He found a tiny, luminous cinder amid an obscure constellation. And after a bit He remembered its name: Earth.

135

When He announced that He had chosen that forgotten place for His vacation, His mother was a bit vexed.

"The hotel situation is bad there," she reminded him. "Don't you remember we had some trouble getting reservations?"

He laughed a little, in His kindly way, and assured her that nearly 2,000 years can make a lot of changes in a man's hostility to man. She walked away, wondering, and pretty soon Michael, an enormous archangel, with a handsome face and the wingspread of a B-29, came up to Him and sat down.

"I heard you're going on a trip," Michael the Archangel said. "I'll drive you down. And get you back in a jiffy."

"No, thanks, Michael," He said. "I'll get down all right. And besides, I've been wanting to try some of the transportation down there. Primitive, isn't it?"

And so, on the morning before Christmas, He arrived in New York City, bought some new clothes, took a look around the town, then caught an air liner. He got off at a fashionable winter resort and applied for a room at a nice hotel.

The man behind the desk looked Him over carefully and shook his head. All booked, the man said. At the next Hotel, the desk clerk said the same thing, and at the next and the next. But the doorman of the last place seemed to take a little pity on Him and suggested that He inquire at a place where a lot of young men, bachelors, mainly, seemed to stay.

They were nice to Him there, especially the lady in charge. She said that the town's hostesses and hosts had just about emptied her place looking for extra men to fill in at the numerous holiday parties being held. And would He please tidy up in a hurry? He did, and was happy when the lady in charge said He too had been invited to a party. It would give Him a chance, he felt, to get to know the descendants of those for whom He had undergone certain hardships.

It was a grand party, and He found it stimulating. Nobody caught his name, but He passed that off as one of the idiosyn-

136

crasies of this odd little planet. The talk was fine: certain political events had bestirred the men; certain fashion events, the women.

He joined in and found it rather easy to hold His own, for people had talked much like that when He was around the last time. Everybody at the party loved His fairness and easy wit.

Everything would have gone nicely, He supposed later, if the talk had not turned to "Where are you from?"

They were from an interesting variety of places, He found; places that had sprung up during the split second of the last two or three centuries. He was charmed by the pride they held in their home towns, their schools, their clubs, and the like. Then just before the party was to move on to the exclusive Wampum Club for dinner, He realized that somebody was asking Him the question.

"I was born in Bethlehem," He said. "It's a small place."

"Bethlehem?" His host repeated. "Been there many times, when I was in steel. Fine town!"

"Then we moved on to a town named Nazareth, and finally to Jerusalem."

He didn't notice, for a moment, that a heavy silence had fallen on the room.

The host was the first to recover, boomed for another round of drinks for the other guests, and then took the Stranger by the arm and escorted Him to a quiet corner of the living room.

"Don't mean to be personal, old man," he said, "but you say you were born in Bethlehem . . . moved to Nazareth . . . then Jerusalem?"

"Yes," He said wonderingly.

"What's your profession?"

He thought a bit then smiled. "I was a carpenter for a time. Then I sort of went on the road, as you say."

"Salesman?"

He thought that over for a time. "Yes, in a way."

137

"We thought you were a writer, from the beard . . ."

He shook his head. "No, I never got around to that. But I used to talk now and then."

The host thought things over for a long time. "Well," he said, finally, "I hope you won't be offended by this, but we've got to face facts here. Are you Jewish?"

"Yes." He smiled.

The host wheezed again. "Facts," he said, "have to be faced. We were counting on you being an extra man at the dinner at the Wampum. But, I'm sorry, it can't be done. There's a rule, see? Don't blame me, I didn't make it. It's just a rule. If I bring you, and they find it out, I'll be asked to resign from the club. It's the oldest and best club around here, and we've got to live here, see? I hope you understand."

"Understand? Why, yes, I guess I do. You've already been quite kind to me . . ."

"Not at all. Not at all. You're interesting. I like your manner. But this is one of those things I can't buck."

The host's wife hovered behind them. "We're late, Horace," she reminded him. "You know how they are about holding tables, especially on Christmas Eve."

The guests crowded out on the curb in happy confusion and piled into their convertibles and the chauffeur-driven cars. The sweet sound of racing motors filled the soft night. The host stayed behind, momentarily, and put his arm around the Visitor's shoulders.

"No hard feelings?" the man asked.

"No hard feelings," He answered warmly.

"Well . . . I got to get along. Nice of you to drop in." The host stepped into his own convertible and roared off.

The Stranger stood for a moment on the curb of the now-darkened street. The air was tender in the palms, and it reminded Him vaguely of the palms He had known as a Child, and the palms He had known for one brief Sunday as a Man.

He thought for a long time, reflectively. Well, a little more time . . . Then He chuckled a bit—or was it a sigh?—and clapped on His new hat.

Then He looked up at the star-studded night and cupped His hands around His sensitive mouth.

"Michael!" He shouted at the top of His lungs. "Oh, Michael!"

By Amos Russel Wells

THE INN THAT MISSED ITS CHANCE
(The Landlord Speaks, A.D. 28)

What could be done? The house was full of folks!
His honor, Marcus Lucius, and his scribes
Who made the census: honorable men
From farthest Galilee, come hitherward
To be enrolled; high ladies and their lords;
The rich, the rabbis, such a noble throng
As Bethlehem had never seen before
And may not see again. And there they were,
Close-herded with their servants, till the inn
Was like a hive at swarming time, and I
Was fairly crazed among them.

                Could I know
That *they* were so important? Just the two,
No servants, just a workman sort of man,
Leading a donkey, and his wife thereon
Drooping and pale,- I saw them not myself,
My servants must have driven them away;
But had I seen them,- how was I to know?
Were inns to welcome stragglers up and down

In all our towns from Beersheba to Dan,
Till He should come? And how were men to know?

There was a sign, they say, a heavenly light
Resplendent: but I had no time for stars,
And there were songs of angels in the air
Out on the hills; but how was I to hear
Amid the thousand clamors of an inn?

Of course, if I had known them, who they were,
And who was He that should be born that night—
For now I learn that they will make him King,
A second David, who will ransom us
From these Philistine Romans—who but He
That feeds an army with a loaf of bread,
And if a soldier falls, He touches him
And up he leaps, uninjured? Had I known,
I would have turned the whole inn upside down,
His honor, Marcus Lucius, and the rest,
And sent them all to stables, had I known.

So you have seen Him, stranger, and perhaps
Again may see Him? Prithee say for me,
I did not know; and if He comes again
As he will surely come, with retinue,
And banners, and an army, tell my Lord
That all my inn is His to make amends.

Alas! Alas! to miss a chance like that!
This inn might be the chief among them all,
The birthplace of Messiah, had I known!

It was a dismal Christmas Eve for the travelers on the almost empty train—until they remembered the TWO greatest Christmas stories ever told.

By Jerome Weidman

THE GREATEST CHRISTMAS
STORY EVER TOLD

ONE winter day more than thirty years ago, just before Christmas holiday in a public school on New York's lower East Side, a second-grade teacher read a story to her pupils.

"Marley was dead——" she began.

I had no way of knowing, of course, that she had uttered three of the most famous words in the English language. Perhaps an hour later, when she finished, even I—then aged seven—was aware that I had made a grave error in judgment: this was *not* just another story.

I have heard people say that they don't know how many times they have read *A Christmas Carol*. It is a difficulty I do not share with them. I know exactly how many times I've read *A Christmas Carol*. In round figures: zero!

But I couldn't possibly saw how often I have *heard* it. For this small masterpiece from the pen of one of the half-dozen greatest novelists the world has ever known is surely one of the most-read-aloud stories of all time.

143

I have heard it in classrooms, from lecture platforms, on the radio, in theaters, on television, in newsreels.

For years no Christmas seemed to me complete until I saw in my newspaper the photograph of the Roosevelt family gathering at Hyde Park, and the Churchill family assembling at Chartwell, to hear the great men read aloud the greatest— certainly the most popular—story Charles Dickens ever wrote.

Why should this simple tale have assumed in the Anglo-Saxon mind a position almost as indispensable as that of holly and mistletoe in the celebration of Christmas?

I believe that much of the enormous popularity of Dickens' *A Christmas Carol* is due to the simple fact that it reads aloud so well.

When I think that I, who have never read the story, know it so intimately, it occurs to me that there must be thousands, perhaps millions, of others whose knowledge was gleaned in similar fashion—by ear.

And this, I think, is an essential part of the spirit of Christmas: nobody—well, *almost* nobody—reads *A Christmas Carol* to himself. Everybody wants to read it aloud to others. Because nobody likes to celebrate Christmas alone.

Home for Christmas. That's where everybody, instinctively, wants to be for the great holiday. And that's where everybody who can manage it goes.

Many people spend more time traveling to and from the place where they celebrate Christmas than they devote to the actual celebration itself.

I find it odd that this simple fact has not received more attention from our creative writers. There is a great deal of published material about the holiday itself. There is very little dramatization of the journey toward it.

This may not seem a particularly important gap in a nation's bookshelves. Indeed the existence of the gap was completely

144

unknown to me during the first quarter century of my existence. Until, one day, a number of years ago, I found myself by sheer accident in the very midst of it.

I had been in Seattle for about a week, doing nothing in particular, and enjoying it enormously. Then, all at once, it seemed terribly important to be in New York. I can't remember why. But I do remember that the weather had grounded all planes, so I left Seattle by train, in a snowstorm, at 8:00 P.M. Pacific Coast Time. And I discovered ten minutes later, to my astonishment, that it was Christmas Eve!

I was a little troubled by my own astonishment. During my week in Seattle, the shop windows had been decorated with tinsel and holly. A Santa Claus, clanging his bell, had been posted at every busy street corner. And in order to reach the elevators in the lobby of my hotel, it had been necessary to detour around a handsome tree, gaily hung with colored lights.

I could hardly claim that I had not, so to speak, been put on notice. And yet—as I ate my dinner in the almost empty dining car and stared at the cheerful waiter who had catapulted me into an awareness of the date by wishing me a Merry Christmas when he handed me the menu—that was precisely the claim I felt like making. Christmas Eve? It didn't seem possible. I had the uneasy feeling that, somehow, I had been cheated.

A half hour later I found I was not the only one on that train who had this feeling. There were, to be precise, three others. The first was Mr. Sawyer.

I found him sitting alone in the club car. He was plump, middle-aged, and neat, and he wore a pince-nez. He looked like a Madison Avenue bank official, but he proved to be a Philadelphia lawyer.

"You know something?" he said after we had introduced ourselves. "This is the first time in my life I've ever been on a train on Christmas Eve." He sounded sorry for himself.

"Me too," I said. It occurred to me that I also sounded sorry for myself.

"I've been on trains and planes the *day* before Christmas," Mr. Sawyer said. "Lots of times. Rushing to get home in time to decorate the tree. But this——" Mr. Sawyer looked out morosely at the gusts of whirling snow that kept smashing noiselessly against the windows of the club car. "This is the first time I've ever had to spend all of Christmas Eve traveling."

I asked how it had happened. He said he had come to Seattle to close a large deal for an important client. But he had assured his wife and children he would be home for the holiday.

Unfortunately, one of the Seattle lawyers on the other side of the deal had proved to be pigheaded. By the time the contract had been signed, it was impossible for Mr. Sawyer to get back to Philadelphia in time.

"That's why I'm here," he said glumly. "On an empty train, in the middle of nowhere."

It wasn't quite that, of course. During the next quarter hour, two other passengers came into the club car to join us: a Mrs. Hollister, and a Mrs. Merton. They felt sorry for themselves too.

"You know what I think," Mr. Sawyer said after the introductions were out of the way. "I think we all ought to have a drink."

It seemed a simple enough suggestion. Until we discovered that Mr. Sawyer had meant eggnog! We all watched with a good deal of astonishment while he rang for the steward, then summoned the conductor, and finally went off for a conference with the chef in the dining car.

Mrs. Hollister was on her way to visit her son in New Haven, where he was studying medicine. According to her original plan, she should have been in New Haven two days ago. An

146

attack of flu, however, had caused Mrs. Hollister to cancel her original reservation, and so here she was, still en route.

Mrs. Merton had been the last of the group to come into the club car. She was a motherly-looking woman with almost white hair and a lieutenant colonel's silver leaf pinned at her throat.

Mrs. Merton told us that she had come all the way from Hawaii, where her husband was stationed, to spend Christmas in Chicago with her aged parents.

Unfortunately, the Army transport that had brought her from Honolulu had docked at Seattle instead of in San Diego, as originally planned. So she missed her airplane connection to Chicago.

By eleven-thirty, Mr. Sawyer had managed to assemble the necessary eggs, nutmeg, sugar, milk, cream and whisky. On the small writing desk of that shaking club car, he was actually making an eggnog, using for his mixing bowl a battered aluminum soup tureen provided by the dining-car chef.

Meanwhile, at the other end of the car, Mrs. Merton and Mrs. Hollister were improvising a Christmas tree. They were making it with a feather duster, which the porter had fetched from his locker, and some bits of colored tin foil from a box of chocolates Mrs. Hollister supplied. Mrs. Merton had stuck the feather duster upright in an empty highball glass. She had wadded the handle tight with crumpled newspaper. And both women were distributing the little bits of colored tin foil throughout the duster as though they were fancy glass balls.

As I glanced from Mr. Sawyer and his eggnog at one end of the club car to Mrs. Merton and Mrs. Hollister and their tree at the other end, it seemed to me there was something familiar about the slightly unreal scene. I couldn't imagine what it was.

Mr. Sawyer stopped fussing with the eggnog. He sampled it, smacked his lips thoughtfully, added a little more whisky,

147

took another taste, and seemed to be satisfied. "Now," he said as he began to fill the glasses, "I'd really like to read you a story, that's what I'd like to do."

I stared in astonishment at the plump, middle-aged man with the pince-nez. All at once I knew what it was about the unreal scene that had seemed familiar. As I took the glass of eggnog Mr. Sawyer held out to me, it was as though the intervening years had vanished and I were back in the second-grade in a public school on New York's lower East Side.

" 'Marley was dead' "——I said.

Mr. Sawyer beamed. Mrs. Hollister nodded and smiled. Mrs. Merton shook her head gently.

" 'Marley was dead, *to begin with*,' " she corrected.

We all nodded.

" 'There is no doubt whatever about that,' " Mrs. Hollister said, taking up the quotation. " 'The register of his burial was signed by the clergyman, the clerk, the undertaker, and the chief mourner.' "

" 'Scrooge signed it,' " I said.

" 'And Scrooge's name was good upon 'Change, for anything he chose to put his hand to,' " added Mrs. Merton.

" 'Old Marley was as dead as a door-nail,' " said Mr. Sawyer, and there was a pause while we all sipped our eggnog. "I said I'd *like* to read you a story," Mr. Sawyer said finally. "Unfortunately, I can't, because my copy is in Philadelphia, where I should be at this moment."

"The copy I would be hearing it from is in Chicago," Mrs. Merton said. "I haven't heard my father read it for nine years."

"I haven't heard it since my husband died," Mrs. Hollister said. "I thought perhaps this year, when at last I got to New Haven, my son might——"

Her voice stopped. We all stared at the whirling gusts of snow that kept whipping past the windows.

"There must be other Christmas stories," Mr. Sawyer said abruptly, with a touch of petulance. "Let's try to think."

We did, recalling many favorites.

"But those are all stories *about* Christmas," Mr. Sawyer said suddenly. "Why doesn't somebody write a story about *getting* to Christmas?"

We all stared at him in puzzlement.

"What do you mean?" said Mrs. Hollister.

"The fact that people are always talking and writing about what happens to them at Christmas," Mr. Sawyer said. "But nobody ever seems to write about the things that happen to people on their *way* to their Christmas celebration."

For the second time that night I stared in surprise at Mr. Sawyer. The point he had raised had never occurred to me before.

"Maybe that's because nothing that happens to people on their way to celebrate Christmas is as interesting as the celebration itself," Mrs. Hollister said.

"I doubt that," Mr. Sawyer said. "People have been traveling to Christmas celebrations almost two thousand years. You can't tell me that in all that time nothing interesting happened to any of them."

I ran swiftly through a list of all the travel books I could bring to mind. Not one dealt with Christmas.

"I'm afraid that must be the answer, though," Mrs. Hollister said. "After all, people who start out for wherever they intend to observe Christmas aren't doing anything unusual. Thousands of people are doing it at the very same time. It's just an ordinary trip. Why should anybody want to write about it?"

"That's not quite true," Mrs. Merton said.

We all looked at the motherly woman with the lieutenant colonel's silver leaf pinned at her throat. She was fishing in her purse.

"I know a very good story that deals with just what we've been talking about," she said. "I'd like to read it to you," she said through her pleasant smile. "It's not very long."

It isn't. But it covers a great deal of ground.

Every year, when the tinsel starts going up in the shop windows, I find myself thinking about that club car speeding through the snowy night, and the extraordinary things that sometimes happen to people who think they are embarking on a perfectly ordinary trip.

From the glowing pages of the Gospel according to Luke, Mrs. Merton has helped me choose for these columns the most extraordinary description that has ever been written about what the participants thought at the time was a perfectly ordinary trip:

And it came to pass in those days, that there went out a decree from Caesar Augustus, that all the world should be taxed. (And this taxing was first made when Cyrenius was governor of Syria.) And all went to be taxed, every one into his own city. And Joseph also went up from Galilee, out of the city of Nazareth, into Judea, unto the city of David, which is called Bethlehem (because he was of the house and lineage of David), to be taxed with Mary his espoused wife, being great with child. And so it was, that, while they were there, the days were accomplished that she should be delivered. And she brought forth her firstborn son, and wrapped him in swaddling clothes, and laid him in a manger; because there was no room for them in the inn.

And there were in the same country shepherds abiding in the field, keeping watch over their flock by night. And, lo, the angel of the Lord came upon them, and the glory of the Lord shone round about them; and they were sore afraid. And the angel said unto them,

"Fear not: for, behold, I bring you good tidings of great joy, which shall be to all people. For unto you is born this day in the city of David a Saviour, which is Christ the Lord. And this shall be a sign unto you; ye shall find the babe wrapped in swaddling clothes, lying in a manger."

And suddenly there was with the angel a multitude of the heavenly host praising God, and saying,

"Glory to God in the highest, and on earth peace, good will toward men."

The following version of A Christmas Carol, *all in Dickens' own words, has been shortened so that it may be read aloud in half an hour.*

By Charles Dickens

A CHRISTMAS CAROL

STAVE ONE

MARLEY was dead, to begin with. There is no doubt whatever about that. The register of his burial was signed by the clergyman, the clerk, the undertaker, and the chief mourner. Scrooge signed it. And Scrooge's name was good upon 'Change, for anything he chose to put his hand to.

Old Marley was as dead as a door-nail.

Scrooge knew he was dead? Of course he did. How could it be otherwise? Scrooge and he were partners for I don't know how many years. Scrooge was his sole executor, his sole administrator, his sole assign, his sole residuary legatee, his sole friend, and sole mourner. And even Scrooge was not so dreadfully cut up by the sad event, but that he was an excellent man of business on the very day of the funeral, and solemnized it with an undoubted bargain.

Oh! But he was a tight-fisted hand at the grindstone, Scrooge! a squeezing, wrenching, grasping, scraping, clutching, covetous, old sinner! Hard and sharp as flint, from which no steel had ever struck out generous fire; secret, and self-contained, and solitary as an oyster. The cold within him froze his old features, nipped his pointed nose, shriveled his cheek, stiffened his gait; made his eyes red, his thin lips blue; and spoke out shrewdly in his grating voice. A frosty rime was on his head, and on his eyebrows, and his wiry chin. He carried his own low temperature always about with him; he iced his office in the dog-days; and didn't thaw it one degree at Christmas.

Nobody ever stopped him in the street to say, with gladsome looks, "My dear Scrooge, how are you? When will you come to see me?"

But what did Scrooge care! It was the very thing he liked—to edge his way along the crowded paths of life, warning all human sympathy to keep its distance.

Once upon a time—of all the good days in the year, on Christmas Eve—old Scrooge sat busy in his counting-house. It was cold, bleak, biting weather, and he could hear the people in the court outside go wheezing up and down, beating their hands upon their breasts, and stamping their feet upon the pavement-stones to warm them. The city clocks had only just gone three, but it was quite dark already, and candles were flaring in the windows of the neighboring offices.

The door of Scrooge's counting-house was open that he might keep his eye upon his clerk, who in a dismal little cell beyond, a sort of tank, was copying letters. Scrooge had a very small fire, but the clerk's fire was so very much smaller that it looked like one coal. But he couldn't replenish it, for Scrooge kept the coal-box in his own room; and so surely as the clerk came in with the shovel the master predicted that it would be necessary for them to part.

"A merry Christmas, uncle! God save you!" cried a cheerful voice. It was the voice of Scrooge's nephew, who had so heated himself with rapid walking in the fog and frost that he was all in a glow; his face was ruddy and handsome; his eyes sparkled.

"Bah!" said Scrooge. "Humbug!"

"Christmas a humbug, uncle!" said Scrooge's nephew. "You don't mean that, I am sure?"

"I do," said Scrooge. "Merry Christmas! What right have you to be merry? You're poor enough."

"Come, then," returned the nephew gaily. "What right have you to be dismal? You're rich enough."

"Nephew!" said the uncle, "keep Christmas in your own way, and let me keep it in mine."

"Keep it!" repeated Scrooge's nephew. "But you don't keep it."

"Let me leave it alone, then," said Scrooge.

"Don't be angry, uncle. Come! Dine with us tomorrow."

Scrooge said that he would see him—yes, indeed he did. He went the whole length of the expression, and said that he would see him in that extremity first.

"But why?" cried Scrooge's nephew. "Why? We have never had any quarrel, to which I have been a party. But I have made the trial in homage to Christmas, and I'll keep my Christmas humor to the last. So a merry Christmas, uncle!"

"Good afternoon!" said Scrooge.

"And a happy New Year!"

"Good afternoon!" said Scrooge.

His nephew left the room without an angry word, notwithstanding. He stopped at the outer door to bestow the greetings of the season on the clerk, who, cold as he was, was warmer than Scrooge; for he returned them cordially.

"There's another fellow," muttered Scrooge, who overheard him: "My clerk, with fifteen shillings a-week, and a wife and family, talking about a merry Christmas. I'll retire to Bedlam."

At length the hour of shutting up the counting-house arrived.

With an ill-will Scrooge dismounted from his stool, and tacitly admitted the fact to the expectant clerk in the Tank, who instantly snuffed his candle out, and put on his hat.

"You'll want all day tomorrow, I suppose," said Scrooge.

"If quite convenient, sir."

"It's not convenient," said Scrooge, "and it's not fair. If I was to stop half-a-crown for it, you'd think yourself ill-used, I'll be bound?"

The clerk smiled faintly.

"And yet," said Scrooge, "you don't think *me* ill-used when I pay a day's wages for no work."

The clerk observed that it was only once a year. "A poor excuse for picking a man's pocket every twenty-fifth of December!" said Scrooge, buttoning his great-coat to the chin. "But I suppose you must have the whole day. Be here all the earlier next morning."

The clerk promised that he would; and Scrooge walked out with a growl. The office was closed in a twinkling, and the clerk, with the long ends of his white comforter dangling below his waist (for he boasted no great-coat) ran home to Camden Town as hard as he could pelt.

Scrooge took his melancholy dinner in his usual melancholy tavern; and having read all the newspapers, and beguiled the rest of the evening with his banker's-book, went home to bed. He lived in chambers which had once belonged to his deceased partner.

Half a dozen gas-lamps out of the street wouldn't have lighted the entry too well, so you may suppose that it was pretty dark. Up Scrooge went, not caring a button for that. Darkness is cheap, and Scrooge liked it. But before he shut his heavy door, he walked through his rooms to see that all was right.

Quite satisfied, he closed his door, and locked himself in; double-locked himself in. Thus secured against surprise, he took off his cravat; put on his dressing-gown and slippers, and his nightcap; and sat down before the fire to take his gruel.

"Humbug!" said Scrooge; and walked across the room.

After several turns, he sat down again. As he threw his head back in the chair, his glance happened to rest upon a bell, a disused bell, that hung in the room, and communicated for some purpose now forgotten with a chamber in the highest story of the building. It was with great astonishment, and with a strange, inexplicable dread, that as he looked, he saw this bell begin to swing. It swung so softly in the outset that it scarcely made a sound; but soon it rang out loudly, and so did every bell in the house.

This might have lasted half a minute, or a minute, but it seemed an hour. The bells ceased as they had begun, together. They were succeeded by a clanking noise, deep down below; as if some person were dragging a heavy chain over the casks in the wine-merchant's cellar.

The cellar-door flew open with a booming sound, and then he heard the noise much louder, on the floors below; then coming up the stairs; then coming towards his door.

"It's humbug still!" said Scrooge. "I won't believe it!"

His color changed, though, when, without a pause, it came on through the heavy door, and passed into the room before his eyes. Upon its coming in, the dying flame leaped up, as though it cried, "I know him! Marley's Ghost!"

The same face! the very same. Marley in his pigtail, usual waistcoat, tights and boots; the tassels on the latter bristling, like his pigtail, and his coat-skirts, and the hair upon his head. The chain he drew was clasped about his middle. It was long, and wound about him like a tail; and it was made of cash-boxes, keys, padlocks, ledgers, deeds, and heavy purses wrought in steel. His body was transparent; so that Scrooge observing him, and looking through his waistcoat, could see the two buttons on his coat behind.

157

"Can you—can you sit down?" asked Scrooge, looking doubt-fully at him.

"I can."

"Do it then."

"You don't believe in me," observed the Ghost.

"I don't," said Scrooge.

"Why do you doubt your senses?"

"Because," said Scrooge, "a little thing affects them. A slight disorder of the stomach makes them cheats. You may be an undigested bit of beef, a blot of mustard, a crumb of cheese, a fragment of underdone potato."

At this the spirit raised a frightful cry, and shook its chain with such a dismal and appalling noise, that Scrooge held on tight to his chair, to save himself from falling in a swoon.

"Mercy!" Scrooge said. "Dreadful apparition, why do you trouble me?"

"Man of the worldly mind!" replied the Ghost, "do you be-lieve in me or not?"

"I do," said Scrooge. "I must. But why do spirits walk the earth, and why do they come to me?"

"It is required of every man," the Ghost returned, "that the spirit within him should walk abroad among his fellowmen, and travel far and wide; and if that spirit goes not forth in life, it is condemned to do so after death. It is doomed to wander through the world—O woe is me!—and witness what it cannot share, but might have shared on earth, and turned to hap-piness!"

"You are fettered," said Scrooge, trembling. "Tell me why?"

"I wear the chain I forged in life," replied the Ghost. "I made it link by link, and yard by yard; I girded it on of my own free will, and of my own free will I wore it. Is its pattern strange to *you*?"

"But you were always a good man of business, Jacob," fal-tered Scrooge, who now began to apply this to himself.

"Business!" cried the Ghost, wringing its hands again. "Mankind was my business. The common welfare was my business; charity, mercy, forbearance, and benevolence were, all, my business. The dealings of my trade were but a drop of water in the comprehensive ocean of my business!"

Scrooge was very much dismayed to hear the specter going on at this rate, and began to quake exceedingly.

"Hear me!" cried the Ghost. "My time is nearly gone. I am here tonight to warn you, that you have yet a chance and hope of escaping my fate. You will be haunted by Three Spirits. Without their visits, you cannot hope to shun the path I tread. Expect the first tomorrow, when the bell tolls One. Expect the second on the next night at the same hour. The third upon the next night when the last stroke of twelve has ceased to vibrate. Look to see me no more; and look that, for your own sake, you remember what has passed between us!"

STAVE TWO

THE FIRST OF THE THREE SPIRITS

When Scrooge awoke, it was so dark, that looking out of bed, he could scarcely distinguish the transparent window from the opaque walls of his chamber. He was endeavoring to pierce the darkness with his ferret eyes, when the chimes of a neighboring church struck with a deep, dull, hollow, melancholy ONE. Light flashed up in the room upon the instant, and the curtains of his bed were drawn aside; and Scrooge, starting up into a half-recumbent attitude, found himself face to face with the unearthly visitor who drew them.

It was a strange figure—like a child: yet not so like a child as like an old man, viewed through some supernatural medium, which gave him the appearance of having receded from the view, and being diminished to a child's proportions. It wore a tunic of the purest white. It held a branch of fresh green holly in its hand; and, in singular contradiction of that wintry emblem, had its dress trimmed with summer flowers. But the strangest thing about it was, that from the crown of its head there sprung a bright clear jet of light, by which all this was visible.

"Who, and what are you?" asked Scrooge.

"I am the Ghost of Christmas Past."

It put out its strong hand as it spoke, and clasped him gently by the arm.

As the words were spoken, they passed through the wall, and stood upon an open country road, with fields on either hand. The city had entirely vanished. The darkness and the mist had vanished with it, for it was a clear, cold, winter day, with snow upon the ground.

"Good Heaven!" said Scrooge, clasping his hands together, as he looked about him. "I was bred in this place. I was a boy here!"

"You recollect the way?" inquired the Spirit.

"Remember it!" cried Scrooge with fervor; "I could walk it blindfold."

They walked along the road, Scrooge recognizing every gate, and post, and tree; until a little market-town appeared in the distance, with its bridge, its church, and winding river. Some shaggy ponies now were seen trotting towards them with boys upon their backs, who called to other boys in country gigs and carts, driven by farmers.

"These are but shadows of the things that have been," said the Ghost. "They have no consciousness of us."

The jocund travelers came on; and as they came, Scrooge knew and named them every one. Why was he rejoiced beyond all bounds to see them? Why was he filled with gladness when

160

he heard them give each other Merry Christmas? What was merry Christmas to Scrooge? Out upon merry Christmas! What good had it ever done to him?

"The school is not quite deserted," said the Ghost. "A solitary child, neglected by his friends, is left there still."

They went, the Ghost and Scrooge, across the hall, to a door at the back of the house. It opened before them, and disclosed a long, bare, melancholy room, made barer still by lines of plain deal forms and desks. At one of these a lonely boy was reading near a feeble fire; and Scrooge sat down upon a form, and wept to see his poor forgotten self as he had used to be.

"Poor boy! I wish—" Scrooge muttered, putting his hand in his pocket, and looking about him, after drying his eyes with his cuff: "but it's too late now."

"What is the matter?" asked the Spirit.

"Nothing," said Scrooge, "—nothing. There was a boy singing a Christmas Carol at my door last night. I should like to have given him something: that's all."

The Ghost smiled thoughtfully, and waved its hands, saying as it did so, "Let us see another Christmas!"

Although they had but that moment left the school behind them, they were now in the busy thoroughfares of a city. It was made plain enough, by the dressing of the shops, that here too it was Christmas time again. The Ghost stopped at a certain warehouse door, and asked Scrooge if he knew it.

"Know it!" said Scrooge. "Wasn't I apprenticed here?"

They went in. At sight of an old gentleman sitting in behind a desk, Scrooge cried in great excitement:

"Why, it's old Fezziwig! Bless his heart; it's Fezziwig alive again!"

Old Fezziwig laid down his pen, and looked up at the clock, which pointed to the hour of seven. He rubbed his hands; adjusted his capacious waistcoat; laughed all over himself, and called out in a comfortable, oily, rich, fat, jovial voice:

161

"Yo ho, there! Ebenezer! Dick!"

Scrooge's former self, now grown a young man, came briskly in, accompanied by his fellow 'prentice.

"Clear away, my lads, and let's have lots of room here! Hilli-ho, Dick! Chirrup, Ebenezer!"

Clear away! There was nothing they wouldn't have cleared away, or couldn't have cleared away, with old Fezziwig looking on. It was done in a minute. Every movable was packed off, the floor was swept and watered, the lamps were trimmed, fuel was heaped upon the fire; and the warehouse was as snug, and warm, and dry, and bright a ball-room as you would desire to see upon a winter's night.

In came a fiddler with a music-book, and tuned like fifty stomach-aches. In came Mrs. Fezziwig, one vast substantial smile. In came the three Miss Fezziwigs, beaming and lovable. In came the six young followers whose hearts they broke. In came all the young men and women employed in the business. In came the housemaid, with her cousin, the baker. In came the cook, with her brother's particular friend, the milkman. In came the boy from over the way, who was suspected of not having board enough from his master, trying to hide himself behind the girl from next door but one, who was proved to have had her ears pulled by her mistress. In they all came, one after another; some shyly, some boldly, some gracefully, some awkwardly, some pushing, some pulling; in they all came, anyhow and everyhow. Away they all went, twenty couples at once; hands half round and back again the other way; down the middle and up again; round and round in various stages of affectionate grouping; old top couple always turning up in the wrong place; new top couple starting off again, as soon as they got there.

There were more dances, and there were forfeits, and more dances, and there was cake, and there was negus, and there was a great piece of Cold Roast, and there was a great piece of Cold Boiled, and there were mincepies, and plenty of beer.

During the whole of this time, Scrooge had acted like a man out of his wits. His heart and soul were in the scene, and with his former self. He corroborated everything, remembered everything, enjoyed everything, and underwent the strangest agitation.

"What is the matter?" asked the Ghost.

"Nothing particular," said Scrooge. "I should like to be able to say a word or two to my clerk just now. That's all."

"My time grows short," observed the Spirit. "Quick!"

Again Scrooge saw himself. He was older now; a man in the prime of life. His face had not the harsh and rigid lines of later years; but it had begun to wear the signs of care and avarice.

He was not alone, but sat by the side of a fair young girl in whose eyes there were tears. "Another idol has displaced me," she said. "If it can cheer and comfort you in time to come, as I would have tried to do, I have not just cause to grieve."

"What Idol has displaced you?" he rejoined.

"A golden one."

She left him, and they parted.

"Spirit!" said Scrooge, "show me no more! Conduct me home."

But the relentless Ghost pinioned him in both his arms, and forced him to observe what happened next.

They were in another scene and place; a room, not very large or handsome, but full of comfort. Near to the winter fire sat a beautiful young girl, so like that last that Scrooge believed it was the same, until he saw *her*, now a comely matron, sitting opposite her daughter. The noise in this room was perfectly tumultuous, for there were more children there than Scrooge in his agitated state of mind could count. But now a knocking at the door was heard, and such a rush immediately ensued to greet the father, who came home laden with Christmas toys

163

and presents. Then the shouting and the struggling, and the onslaught that was made! The scaling him, with chairs for ladders, to dive into his pockets, despoil him of brown-paper parcels, hold on tight by his cravat, hug him round his neck, pommel his back, and kick his legs in irrepressible affection!

"Spirit!" said Scrooge, in a broken voice, "remove me from this place."

"I told you these were shadows of the things that have been," said the Ghost. "That they are what they are, do not blame me!"

"Remove me!" Scrooge exclaimed. "I cannot bear it! Leave me! Take me back! Haunt me no longer!"

STAVE THREE

THE SECOND OF THE THREE GHOSTS

Awaking in the middle of a prodigiously tough snore, and sitting up in bed to get his thoughts together, Scrooge had no occasion to be told that the bell was again upon the stroke of One.

It was his own room. There was no doubt about that. But it had undergone a surprising transformation. The walls and ceiling were so hung with living green, that it looked a perfect grove; from every part of which, bright gleaming berries glistened, and such a mighty blaze went roaring up the chimney, as that dull petrification of a hearth had never known in Scrooge's time. Beside it in easy state there sat a jolly Giant, glorious to see.

"I am the Ghost of Christmas Present," said the Spirit. "Touch my robe!"

Scrooge did as he was told, and held it fast.

Holly, mistletoe, red berries, ivy, all vanished instantly. So

164

did the room, the fire, the ruddy glow, the hour of night; and they stood in the city streets on Christmas morning, where the steeples called good people all to church and chapel, and away they came, flocking through the streets in their best clothes, and with their gayest faces.

Scrooge and the Ghost went on, invisible, into the suburbs of the town, straight to the house of Scrooge's clerk.

Then up rose Mrs. Cratchit, Cratchit's wife, dressed out but poorly in a twice-turned gown, but brave in ribbons, which are cheap and make a goodly show for sixpence; and she laid the cloth, assisted by Belinda Cratchit, second of her daughters, also brave in ribbons; while Master Peter Cratchit plunged a fork into the saucepan of potatoes, and getting the corners of his monstrous shirt-collar (Bob's private property, conferred upon his son and heir in honor of the day) into his mouth, rejoiced to find himself so gallantly attired. Now two smaller Cratchits, boy and girl, came tearing in, screaming that outside the baker's they had smelt the goose! Master Peter Cratchit blew the fire, until the slow potatoes, bubbling up, knocked loudly at the saucepan-lid to be let out and peeled.

"What has ever got your precious father then?" said Mrs. Cratchit. "And your brother, Tiny Tim! And Martha warn't as late last Christmas Day by half an hour!"

"Here's Martha, mother," said a girl appearing as she spoke. "Here's Martha, mother!" cried the two young Cratchits. "Hurrah! There's *such* a goose, Martha!"

"Why, bless your heart alive, my dear, how late you are!" said Mrs. Cratchit, kissing her. "Sit ye down before the fire, my dear, and have a warm, Lord bless ye!"

"No, no! There's father coming," cried the two young Cratchits, who were everywhere at once. "Hide, Martha, hide!"

So Martha hid herself, and in came little Bob, the father, with at least three feet of comforter, exclusive of the fringe, hanging down before him; and his threadbare clothes darned up and brushed, to look seasonable; and Tiny Tim upon his shoulder. Alas for Tiny Tim, he bore a little crutch, and had his limbs supported by an iron frame!

"Why, where's our Martha?" cried Bob Cratchit, looking round.

"Not coming," said Mrs. Cratchit.

"Not coming!" said Bob, with a sudden declension in his high spirits. "Not coming upon Christmas Day!" Martha didn't like to see him disappointed, if it were only in joke; so she came out prematurely from behind the closet door, and ran into his arms, while the two young Cratchits hustled Tiny Tim, and bore him off into the wash-house, that he might hear the pudding singing in the copper.

"And how did little Tim behave?" asked Mrs. Cratchit, when she had rallied Bob on his credulity, and Bob had hugged his daughter to his heart's content.

"As good as gold," said Bob, "and better. Somehow he gets thoughtful, sitting by himself so much, and thinks the strangest things you ever heard. He told me, coming home, that he hoped the people saw him in the church, because he was a cripple, and it might be pleasant to them to remember, upon Christmas Day, who made lame beggars walk and blind men see."

Bob's voice was tremulous when he told them this, and trembled more when he said that Tiny Tim was growing strong and hearty.

Back came Tiny Tim before another word was spoken, escorted by his brother and sister to his stool beside the fire; and while Bob compounded some hot mixture in a jug with gin and lemons, and stirred it round and round and put it on the hob to simmer, Master Peter and the two ubiquitous young Cratchits went to fetch the goose, with which they soon returned in high procession.

Such a bustle ensued that you might have thought a goose the rarest of all birds; a feathered phenomenon, to which a black swan was a matter of course—and in truth it was something very like it in that house. Mrs. Cratchit made the gravy; Master Peter mashed the potatoes with incredible vigor; Miss Belinda sweetened up the applesauce; Martha dusted the hot plates; Bob took Tiny Tim beside him in a tiny corner at the table; the two young Cratchits set chairs for everybody, and mounting guard upon their posts, crammed spoons into their mouths, lest they should shriek for goose before their turn came to be helped.

At last the dishes were set on, and grace was said. It was succeeded by a breathless pause, as Mrs. Cratchit, looking slowly all along the carving-knife, prepared to plunge it in the breast; but when she did, and when the long-expected gush of stuffing issued forth, one murmur of delight arose all round the board, and even Tiny Tim, excited by the two young Cratchits, beat on the table with the handle of his knife, and feebly cried Hurrah!

There never was such a goose. Bob said he didn't believe there ever was such a goose cooked. Its tenderness and flavor, size and cheapness, were the themes of universal admiration. Eked out by applesauce and mashed potatoes, it was a sufficient dinner for the whole family; indeed, as Mrs. Cratchit said with great delight (surveying one small atom of a bone upon the dish), they hadn't ate it all at last! Yet every one had had enough, and the youngest Cratchits in particular were steeped in sage and onion to the eyebrows! But now, the plates being changed by Miss Belinda, Mrs. Cratchit left the room alone— too nervous to bear witness—to take the pudding up, and bring it in.

Suppose it should not be done enough! Suppose it should break in turning out! Suppose somebody should have got over the wall of the back-yard, and stolen it, while they were merry with the goose—a supposition at which the two young Cratchits became livid! All sorts of horrors were supposed.

167

Hallo! A great deal of steam! The pudding was out of the copper. A smell like a washing-day! That was the cloth. A smell like an eatinghouse and a pastrycook's next door to each other, with a laundress's next door to that! That was the pudding! In half a minute Mrs. Cratchit entered—flushed, but smiling proudly—with the pudding, like a speckled cannon-ball, so hard and firm, blazing in half of half-a-quartern of ignited brandy, and bedight with Christmas holly stuck into the top.

O, a wonderful pudding! Bob Cratchit said, and calmly too, that he regarded it as the greatest success achieved by Mrs. Cratchit since their marriage. Mrs. Cratchit said that, now the weight was off her mind, she would confess she had had her doubts about the quantity of flour. Everybody had something to say about it, but nobody said or thought it was at all a small pudding for a large family. It would have been flat heresy to do so. Any Cratchit would have blushed to hint at such a thing.

At last the dinner was all done, the cloth was cleared, the hearth swept, and the fire made up. Then all the Cratchit family drew round the hearth, in what Bob Cratchit called a circle, meaning half a one; and at Bob Cratchit's elbow stood the family display of glass—two tumblers, and a custard-cup without a handle.

These held the hot stuff from the jug, however, as well as golden goblets would have done; and Bob served it out with beaming looks; while the chestnuts on the fire sputtered and crackled noisily. Then Bob proposed:

"A merry Christmas to us all, my dears. God bless us!"

Which all the family re-echoed.

"God bless us every one!" said Tiny Tim, the last of all.

He sat very close to his father's side, upon his little stool. Bob held his withered little hand in his, as if he loved the child, and wished to keep him by his side, and dreaded that he might be taken from him.

"Spirit," said Scrooge, with an interest he had never felt before, "tell me if Tiny Tim will live."

"I see a vacant seat," replied the Ghost, "in the poor chimney-corner, and a crutch without an owner, carefully preserved. If these shadows remain unaltered by the Future, the child will die."

"No, no," said Scrooge. "O, no, kind Spirit! Say he will be spared."

"If these shadows remain unaltered by the Future, none other of my race," returned the Ghost, "will find him here."

"Mr. Scrooge!" said Bob; "I'll give you Mr. Scrooge, the Founder of the Feast!"

"The Founder of the Feast indeed!" cried Mrs. Cratchit, reddening. "I wish I had him here. I'd give him a piece of my mind to feast upon, and I hope he'd have a good appetite for it. Such an odious, stingy, hard, unfeeling man! You know he is, Robert! Nobody knows it better than you do, poor fellow!"

"My dear," was Bob's mild answer, "Christmas Day."

"I'll drink his health for your sake, and the Day's," said Mrs. Cratchit, "not for his."

The children drank the toast after her. It was the first of their proceedings which had no heartiness in it. Scrooge was the Ogre of the family. The mention of his name cast a dark shadow on the party, which was not dispelled for full five minutes. After it had passed away, they were ten times merrier than before, from the mere relief of Scrooge the Baleful being done with.

By this time it was getting dark, and snowing pretty heavily; and as Scrooge and the Spirit went along the streets, the brightness of the roaring fires in kitchens, parlors, and all sorts of rooms was wonderful.

It was a great surprise to Scrooge to hear a hearty laugh. It was a much greater surprise to Scrooge to recognize it as his own nephew's, and to find himself in a bright, dry, gleaming room, with the Spirit standing by his side, and looking at that same nephew with approving affability!

"Ha, ha!" laughed Scrooge's nephew. "Ha, ha, ha! He said that Christmas was a humbug, as I live!"

"More shame for him, Fred!" said Scrooge's niece, indignantly.

She was very pretty: exceedingly pretty. With a dimpled, surprised-looking, capital face; a ripe little mouth, that seemed made to be kissed—as no doubt it was; and the sunniest pair of eyes you ever saw in any little creature's head.

"He's a comical old fellow," said Scrooge's nephew, "that's the truth; and not so pleasant as he might be. However, his offences carry their own punishment. Who suffers by his ill whim? Himself, always. He takes it into his head to dislike us, and he won't come and dine with us. What's the consequence? He don't lose much of a dinner!"

"Indeed, I think he loses a very good dinner," interrupted Scrooge's niece. Everybody else said the same, and they must be allowed to have been competent judges, because they had just had dinner; and, with the dessert upon the table, were clustered round the fire by lamp-light.

"Well! I am very glad to hear it," said Scrooge's nephew, "because I haven't any great faith in these young housekeepers. What do *you* say, Topper?"

Topper had clearly got his eye upon one of Scrooge's niece's sisters, for he answered that a bachelor was a wretched outcast, who had no right to express an opinion on the subject. Whereat Scrooge's niece's sister—the plump one with the lace tucker, not the one with the roses—blushed.

After tea, they had some music. They played at forfeits. There was a game at blind-man's buff. And I no more believe Topper was really blind than I believe he had eyes in his boots. My opinion is, that it was a done thing between him and Scrooge's nephew; and that the Ghost of Christmas Present knew it. The way he went after the plump sister in the lace tucker was an outrage on the credulity of human nature. Knocking down the fire-irons, tumbling over the chairs, bumping up against the piano, smothering himself among the curtains, wherever she went, there went he! He always knew where the plump sister was. He wouldn't catch anybody else! There might have been twenty people there, young and old, but they all played forfeits and so did Scrooge; for, wholly forgetting in the interest he had in what was going on, that his voice made no sound in their ears, he sometimes came out with his guess quite loud, and very often guessed right, too; for the sharpest needle was no sharper than Scrooge. He begged like a boy to be allowed to stay until the guests departed.

"Here's a new game," said Scrooge. "One half-hour, Spirit, only one!"

It was a game called Yes and No, where Scrooge's nephew had to think of something, and the rest must find out what; he only answered to their questions yes or no, as the case was. The brisk fire of questioning to which he was exposed, elicited from him that he was thinking of an animal, a live animal, rather a disagreeable animal, a savage animal, an animal that growled and grunted sometimes, and talked sometimes, and lived in London, and walked about the streets, and wasn't made a show of, and wasn't led by anybody, and didn't live in a menagerie, and was never killed in a market, and was not a horse, or an ass, or a cow, or a bull, or a tiger, or a dog, or a pig, or a cat, or a bear.

At every fresh question that was put to him, this nephew burst into a fresh roar of laughter. At last the plump sister cried, "I have found it out! I know what it is, it's your Uncle Scro-o-o-oge!"

"He has given us plenty of merriment, I am sure," said Fred, "and it would be ungrateful not to drink his health. Here is a glass of mulled wine ready to our hand at the moment; and I say, 'Uncle Scrooge!'"

"Well! Uncle Scrooge!" they cried.

"A merry Christmas and a happy New Year to the old man, whatever he is!" said Scrooge's nephew. "He wouldn't take it from me, but may he have it nevertheless. Uncle Scrooge!"

The bell struck twelve.

Scrooge looked about him for the Ghost and saw it not. As the last stroke ceased to vibrate, he remembered the prediction of old Jacob Marley, and lifting up his eyes, beheld a solemn Phantom, draped and hooded, coming, like a mist along the ground, towards him.

STAVE FOUR

THE LAST OF THE SPIRITS

The Phantom slowly, gravely, silently, approached. It was shrouded in a deep black garment, which concealed its head, its face, its form, and left nothing of it visible save one outstretched hand.

"I am in the presence of the Ghost of Christmas Yet To Come!" said Scrooge.

The Spirit answered not, but pointed onward with its hand and away as it had come towards him. Scrooge followed in the shadow of its dress, which bore him up, he thought, and carried him along.

They scarcely seemed to enter the city; for the city rather seemed to spring up about them, and encompass them of its own act. But there they were, in the heart of it; on 'Change, amongst the merchants; who hurried up and down, and chinked the money in their pockets, and conversed in groups, and looked at their watches, and trifled thoughtfully with their great gold seals. The Spirit stopped beside one little knot of business men. Observing that the hand was pointed to them, Scrooge advanced to listen to their talk.

"No," said a great fat man, "I don't know much about it, either way. I only know he's dead, and that it's likely to be a very cheap funeral, for upon my life I don't know of anybody to go to it."

Speakers and listeners strolled away, and mixed with other groups. Scrooge knew the men, and looked towards the Spirit for an explanation. The Phantom glided on into a street. Its finger pointed to two persons meeting. Scrooge listened again, thinking that the explanation might lie here. He knew these men, also, perfectly. They were men of business: very wealthy, and of great importance. He had made a point always of standing well in their esteem: in a business point of view, that is; strictly in a business point of view.

"Well!" said the first. "Old Scratch has got his own at last, hey?"

"So I am told," returned the second. "Cold, isn't it!"

"Seasonable for Christmas time. You're not a skater, I suppose?"

"No. No. Something else to think of. Good morning!"

Not another word. That was their meeting, their conversation, and their parting.

They left the busy scene, and went into an obscure part of the town, which Scrooge had never penetrated before, although he recognized its situation, and its bad repute. In this den of infamous resort, there was a low-browed, beetling shop, where iron, old rags, bottles, bones and greasy offal were bought. Sitting in among the wares he dealt in, by a charcoal stove, made of old bricks, was a gray-haired rascal. Scrooge and the Phantom came into the presence of this man, just as a woman with a heavy bundle slunk into the shop. He went down on his knees for the greater convenience of opening it, and having unfastened a great many knots, dragged out a large and heavy roll of some dark stuff.

"What do you call this?" said Joe. "Bedcurtains! You don't mean to say you took 'em down with him lying there?"

"Why not?" replied the woman. "He isn't likely to take cold without 'em, I dare say."

"Spirit!" said Scrooge, shuddering from head to foot. "I see, I see. The case of this unhappy man might be my own. My life tends that way, now. Merciful Heaven, what is this!"

He recoiled in terror, for the scene had changed, and now he almost touched a bed—a bare, uncurtained bed, on which, beneath a sheet, there lay a something covered up, which, though it was dumb, announced itself in awful language.

The room was very dark, too dark to be observed with any accuracy. A pale light, rising in the outer air, fell straight upon the bed; and on it, plundered and bereft, unwatched, unwept, uncared for, was the body of this man.

"Spirit!" he said, "this is a fearful place. If there is any person in the town who feels emotion caused by this man's death," said Scrooge, quite agonized, "show that person to me, Spirit, I beseech you!"

The Phantom spread its dark robe before him for a moment, like a wing; and withdrawing it, revealed a room by daylight, where a mother and her children were.

She was expecting some one, and with anxious eagerness: for she walked up and down the room; started at every sound; looked out from the window; glanced at the clock; tried, but in vain, to work with her needle; and could hardly bear the voices of the children in their play.

At length the long-expected knock was heard. She hurried to the door, and met her husband; a man whose face was careworn and depressed, though he was young. There was a remarkable expression in it now; a kind of serious delight of which he felt ashamed, and which he struggled to repress.

He sat down to the dinner that had been hoarding for him by the fire; and when she asked him faintly what news he appeared embarrassed how to answer. "Is it good," she said, "or bad?"

"Bad," he answered.

"We are quite ruined?"

"No. There is hope yet, Caroline."

"If *he* relents," she said.

"He is past relenting," said her husband. "He is dead."

She was a mild and patient creature if her face spoke truth; but she was thankful in her soul to hear it, and she said so, with clasped hands. She prayed forgiveness the next moment, and was sorry; but the first was the emotion of her heart.

"To whom will our debt be transferred?"

"I don't know. But before that time we shall be ready with the money; and even though we were not, it would be bad fortune indeed to find so merciless a creditor in his successor. We may sleep tonight with light hearts, Caroline!"

Yes. Soften it as they would, their hearts were lighter, and it was a happier house for this man's death! The only emotion that the Ghost could show him, caused by the event, was one of pleasure.

"Let me see some tenderness connected with a death," said Scrooge, "or that dark chamber, Spirit, which we left just now, will be forever present to me."

The Ghost conducted him through several streets familiar to his feet. They entered poor Bob Cratchit's house, and found the mother and the children seated round the fire. Quiet. Very quiet. The noisy little Cratchits were as still as statues in one corner, and sat looking up at Peter, who had a book before him. The mother and her daughters were engaged in sewing. But surely they were very quiet!

The mother laid her work upon the table, and put her hand up to her face. "The color hurts my eyes," she said.

The color? Ah, poor Tiny Tim!

"They're better now again," said Cratchit's wife. "It makes them weak by candlelight; and I wouldn't show weak eyes to your father when he comes home, for the world. It must be near his time."

"Past it rather," Peter answered, shutting up his book. "But

I think he has walked a little slower than he used, these few last evenings, mother."

"I have known him walk with—I have known him walk with Tiny Tim upon his shoulder very fast indeed! But he was very light to carry," she resumed, intent upon her work, "and his father loved him so, that it was no trouble—no trouble. And there is your father at the door!"

She hurried out to meet him; and little Bob in his comforter—he had need of it, poor fellow—came in. His tea was ready for him on the hob, and they all tried who should help him to it most. Then the two young Cratchits got up on his knees and laid, each child, a little cheek against his face, as if they said, "Don't mind it, father. Don't be grieved!"

He broke down all at once. He couldn't help it. "My little, little child!" cried Bob—"my little child! When we recollect how patient and how mild he was, although he was a little, little child, we shall not quarrel easily among ourselves, and forget poor Tiny Tim in doing it."

Mrs. Cratchit kissed him, his daughters kissed him, the two young Cratchits kissed him, and Peter and himself shook hands. Spirit of Tiny Tim, thy childish essence was from God!

"Specter," said Scrooge, "something informs me that our parting moment is at hand. I know it, but I know not how. Tell me what man that was whom we saw lying dead."

The Ghost of Christmas Yet To Come conveyed him, as before—though at a different time, he thought; indeed, there seemed no order in these latter visions, save that they were in the Future.

A churchyard.

The Spirit stood among the graves, and pointed to one. Scrooge crept towards it, trembling as he went; and following the finger, read upon the stone of the neglected grave his own name, EBENEZER SCROOGE.

176

"No, Spirit! O, no, no!"

The finger still was there.

"Spirit!" he cried, tight clutching at its robe, "hear me! I am not the man I was. I will not be the man I must have been but for this intercourse. Why show me this, if I am past all hope?"

In his agony, he caught the spectral hand. It sought to free itself, but he was strong in his entreaty, and detained it. The Spirit, stronger yet, repulsed him.

Holding up his hands in one last prayer to have his fate reversed, he saw an alteration in the Phantom's hood and dress. It shrunk, collapsed, and dwindled down into a bedpost.

STAVE FIVE

THE END OF IT

Yes! and the bedpost was his own. The bed was his own, the room was his own. Best and happiest of all, the Time before him was his own, to make amends in!

"I will live in the Past, the Present, and the Future!" Scrooge repeated, as he scrambled out of bed.

He was so fluttered and so glowing with his good intentions, that his broken voice would scarcely answer to his call. He had been sobbing violently in his conflict with the Spirit, and his face was wet with tears.

His hands were busy with his garments all this time; turning them inside out, putting them on upside down, tearing them, mislaying them, making them parties to every kind of extravagance.

"I don't know what to do!" cried Scrooge, laughing and crying in the same breath; and making a perfect Laöcoon of himself with his stockings. "I am as light as a feather, I am as

177

happy as an angel, I am as merry as a schoolboy. I am as giddy as a drunken man. A merry Christmas to everybody! A happy New Year to all the world. Hallo here! Whoop! Hallo!"

Running to the window, he opened it, and put out his head. No fog, no mist; clear, bright, jovial, stirring, cold; cold, piping for the blood to dance to; golden sunlight, Heavenly sky; sweet fresh air; merry bells. O glorious, glorious!

"What's today?" cried Scrooge, calling downward to a boy in Sunday clothes, who perhaps had loitered in to look about him.

"Today!" replied the boy. "Why, CHRISTMAS DAY!"

"It's Christmas Day!" said Scrooge to himself. "I haven't missed it. The Spirits have done it all in one night! Hallo, my fine fellow! Do you know the Poulterer's, in the next street but one, at the corner?"

"I should hope I did," replied the lad.

"An intelligent boy!" said Scrooge. "A remarkable boy! Do you know whether they've sold the prize Turkey that was hanging up there?—Not the little prize Turkey, the big one?"

"What, the one as big as me?" returned the boy.

"What a delightful boy!" said Scrooge. "It's a pleasure to talk to him. Yes, my buck!"

"It's hanging there now," replied the boy.

"It is?" said Scrooge. "Go and buy it. Come back with the man, and I'll give you a shilling. Come back with him in less than five minutes, and I'll give you half a crown!"

The boy was off like a shot.

"I'll send it to Bob Cratchit's!" whispered Scrooge, rubbing his hands, and splitting with a laugh. "He sha'n't know who sends it. It's twice the size of Tiny Tim!"

The hand in which he wrote the address was not a steady one, but write it he did, somehow, and went down stairs to open the street door, ready for the coming of the poulterer's man.

It *was* a Turkey. He never could have stood upon his legs, that bird. He would have snapped 'em short off in a minute, like sticks of sealingwax.

"Why, it's impossible to carry that to Camden Town," said Scrooge. "You must have a cab."

The chuckle with which he said this, and the chuckle with which he paid for the Turkey, and the chuckle with which he paid for the cab, and the chuckle with which he recompensed the boy, were only to be exceeded by the chuckle with which he sat down breathless in his chair again, and chuckled till he cried.

He dressed himself "all in his best," and at last got out into the streets. The people were by this time pouring forth. Walking with his hands behind him, Scrooge regarded every one with a delightful smile. He looked so irresistibly pleasant that three or four good-humored fellows said, "Good morning, sir! A merry Christmas to you!" And Scrooge said often afterwards, that of all the blithe sounds he had ever heard, those were the blithest in his ears.

He went to church, and walked about the streets, and watched the people hurrying to and fro, and patted children on the head, and looked down into the kitchen of houses, and up to the windows; and found that everything could yield him pleasure. In the afternoon, he turned his steps towards his nephew's house.

He passed the door a dozen times before he had the courage to go up and knock. But he made a dash, and did it.

"It's I. Your uncle Scrooge. I have come to dinner. Will you let me in, Fred?"

Let him in! It is a mercy he didn't shake his arm off. He was at home in five minutes. Nothing could be heartier. His niece looked just the same. So did Topper when *he* came. So did the plump sister, when *she* came. So did every one, when

179

they came. Wonderful party, wonderful games, wonderful unanimity, won-der-ful happiness!

But he was early at the office next morning. O, he was early there. If he could only be there first, and catch Bob Cratchit coming late!

And he did it; yes, he did! The clock struck nine. No Bob. A quarter past. No Bob. He was full eighteen minutes and a half behind his time. His hat was off before he opened the door; his comforter too. He was on his stool in a jiffy; driving away with his pen, as if he were trying to overtake nine o'clock.

"Hallo!" growled Scrooge, in his accustomed voice as near as he could feign it. "What do you mean by coming here at this time of day?"

"I am very sorry, sir, I *am* behind—but it's only once a year, sir," pleaded Bob.

"Now, I'll tell you what, my friend," said Scrooge; "I am not going to stand for this sort of thing any longer. And therefore," he continued, leaping from his stool, and giving Bob such a dig in the waistcoat that he staggered back into the Tank again—"and therefore I am about to raise your salary!"

Bob trembled, and got a little nearer to the ruler. He had a momentary idea of knocking Scrooge down with it, holding him, and calling to the people in the court for help and a strait-waistcoat.

"A merry Christmas, Bob!" said Scrooge, with an earnestness that could not be mistaken, as he clapped him on the back. "A merrier Christmas, Bob, my good fellow, than I have given you for many a year! I'll raise your salary, and endeavor to assist your struggling family, and we will discuss your affairs this very afternoon, over a Christmas bowl of smoking bishop, Bob! Make up the fires, and buy another coal-scuttle before you dot another i, Bob Cratchit!"

Scrooge was better than his word. He did it all, and infinitely more; and to Tiny Tim, who did NOT die, he was a second father. He became as good a friend, as good a master, and as good a man as the good old city knew, or any other good old city, town, or borough, in the good old world. Some people laughed to see the alteration in him, but he let them laugh, and little heeded them; for he was wise enough to know that nothing ever happened on this globe, for good, at which some people did not have their fill of laughter in the outset; and knowing that such as these would be blind anyway, he thought it quite as well that they should wrinkle up their eyes in grins, as have the malady in less attractive forms. His own heart laughed, and that was quite enough for him.

He had no further intercourse with Spirits, but ever afterwards it was always said of him that he knew how to keep Christmas well, if any man alive possessed the knowledge. May that be truly said of us, and all of us!

AMEN!

"Done in the manner, if not the spirit, of Dickens"

By *Robert C. Benchley*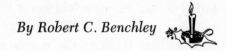

CHRISTMAS AFTERNOON

WHAT an afternoon! Mr. Gummidge said
that, in his estimation, there never had *been* such an afternoon
since the world began, a sentiment which was heartily endorsed
by Mrs. Gummidge and all the little Gummidges, not to mention the relatives who had come over from Jersey for the day.

In the first place, there was the *ennui*. And such *ennui* as it
was! A heavy, overpowering *ennui* such as results from a par-
ticipation in eight courses of steaming, gravied food, topping
off with salted nuts which little old spinster Gummidge from
Oak Hill said she never knew when to stop eating—and true
enough she didn't—a dragging, devitalizing *ennui*, which left
its victims strewn about the living room in various attitudes
of prostration suggestive of those of the petrified occupants in
a newly unearthed Pompeiian dwelling; an *ennui* which carried
with it a retinue of yawns, snarls and thinly veiled insults, and
which ended in ruptures in the clan spirit serious enough to
last throughout the glad new year.

Then there were the toys! Three and a quarter dozen toys
to be divided among seven children. Surely enough, you and I
might say, to satisfy the little tots. But that would be because
we didn't know the tots. In came Baby Lester Gummidge, Lil-

183

lian's boy, dragging an electric grain-elevator which happened
to be the only toy in the entire collection which appealed to
little Norman, five-year-old son of Luther, who lived in Rahway.
In came curly-headed Effie in frantic and throaty disputation
with Arthur, Jr., over the possession of an articulated zebra.
In came Everett, bearing a mechanical negro which would no
longer dance, owing to a previous forcible feeding by the baby
of a marshmallow into its only available aperture. In came
Fonlansbee, teeth buried in the hand of little Ormond, which
bore a popular but battered remnant of what had once been
the proud false-bosom of a hussar's uniform. In they all came,
one after another, some crying, some snapping, some pulling,
some pushing—all appealing to their respective parents for
aid in their intra-mural warfare.

And the cigar smoke! Mrs. Gummidge said she didn't mind
the smoke from a good cigarette, but would they mind if she
opened the windows for just a minute in order to clear the room
of the heavy aroma of used cigars? Mr. Gummidge stoutly
maintained that they were good cigars. His brother, George
Gummidge, said that he, likewise, would say they were. At
which colloquial sally both the Gummidge brothers laughed
testily, thereby breaking the laughter record for the afternoon.

Aunt Libbie, who lived with George, remarked from the dark
corner of the room that it seemed just like Sunday to her. An
amendment was offered to this statement by the cousin, who
was in the insurance business, stating that it was worse than
Sunday. Murmurings indicative of as hearty agreement with
this sentiment as their lethargy would allow came from other
members of the family circle, causing Mr. Gummidge to suggest
a walk in the air to settle their dinner.

And then rose such a chorus of protestations as has seldom
been heard. It was too cloudy to walk. It was too raw. It
looked like snow. It looked like rain. Luther Gummidge said
that he must be starting along home soon, anyway, bringing

forth the acrid query from Mrs. Gummidge as to whether or not he was bored. Lillian said that she felt a cold coming on, and added that something they had had for dinner must have been undercooked. And so it went, back and forth, forth and back, up and down, and in and out, until Mr. Gummidge's suggestion of a walk in the air was reduced to a tattered impossibility and the entire company glowed with ill-feeling.

In the meantime, we must not forget the children. No one else could. Aunt Libbie said that she didn't think there was anything like children to make a Christmas; to which Uncle Ray, the one with the Masonic fob, said, "No, thank God!" Although Christmas is supposed to be a season of good cheer, you (or I, for that matter) couldn't have told, from listening to the little ones, but what it was the children's Armageddon season, when Nature had decreed that only the fittest should survive, in order that the race might be carried on by the strongest, the most predatory and those possessing the best protective coloring. Although there were constant admonitions to Fonlansbee to "Let Ormond have it now; it's his," and to Arthur, Jr., not to be selfish, but to "give the kiddie-car to Effie; she's smaller than you are," the net result was always that Fonlansbee kept the whistle and Arthur, Jr., rode in permanent, albeit disputed, possession of the kiddie-car. Oh, that we mortals should set ourselves up against the inscrutable workings of Nature!

Hallo! A great deal of commotion! That was Uncle George stumbling over the electric train, which had early in the afternoon ceased to function and which had been left directly across the threshold. A great deal of crying! That was Arthur, Jr., bewailing the destruction of his already useless train, about which he had forgotten until the present moment. A great deal of recrimination! That was Arthur, Sr., and George fixing it up. And finally a great crashing! That was Baby Lester pulling over the tree on top of himself, necessitating the bringing to bear of all of Uncle Ray's knowledge of forestry to extricate him from the wreckage.

And finally Mrs. Gummidge passed the Christmas candy around. Mr. Gummidge afterward admitted that this was a tactical error on the part of his spouse. I no more believe that Mrs. Gummidge thought that they wanted that Christmas candy than I believe that she thought they wanted the cold turkey which she later suggested. My opinion is that she wanted to drive them home. At any rate, that is what she succeeded in doing. Such cries as there were of "Ugh! Don't let me see another thing to eat!" and "Take it away!" Then came hurried scramblings in the coat-closet for overshoes. There were the rasping sounds made by cross parents when putting wraps on children. There were insincere exhortations to "come and see us soon" and to "get together for lunch some time." And, finally, there were slammings of doors and the silence of utter exhaustion, while Mrs. Gummidge went about picking up stray sheets of wrapping paper.

And, as Tiny Tim might say in speaking of Christmas afternoon as an institution, "God help us, every one."

"Somehow it just doesn't feel like Christmas."

ACKNOWLEDGMENTS

The co-operation of many individuals and publishing houses is needed in order to compile any anthology. My special thanks is extended to those people and houses who so graciously granted me permission to include the following in this anthology:

"Open Before Christmas," by John MacDonald. Copyright © 1956 by the Crowell-Collier Publishing Company.

"The Boy Who Laughed at Santa Claus," from *A Family Reunion* by Ogden Nash. Copyright © 1942 by Ogden Nash. Reprinted by permission of Little, Brown & Co.

"The Day They Gave Babies Away," by Dale Eunson, illustrated by Fritz Kredel. Used by permission of the publisher, Farrar, Strauss and Cudahy, Inc.

"The Night We Talked to Santa Claus," by Lynn Lofting. Copyright © 1956 by Lynn Lofting.

"A Miserable Merry Christmas," by Lincoln Steffens, from *The Autobiography of Lincoln Steffens*. Copyright © 1931 by Harcourt, Brace and Company, Inc.; renewed by Peter Steffens. Reprinted by permission of the publishers.

"The Best Things Come in Small Packages," from *Junior Miss* by Sally Benson. Copyright © 1939, 1941, by Sally Benson.

"On your toes, Potter. Here comes the supervisor."